AN ATLAS OF THE DOMESTIC TURKEY

(MELEAGRIS GALLOPAVO)

MYOLOGY AND OSTEOLOGY

by

E. B. HARVEY

U. S. Atomic Energy Commission, Germantown, Maryland

H. E. KAISER

Department of Anatomy, School of Medicine

The George Washington University, Washington, D. C.

and

L. E. ROSENBERG

Department of Zoology, University of California, Davis, California

AN ATLAS OF THE DOMESTIC TURKEY

Myology and Osteology

PREFACE

This Atlas is designed to bring into one publication labeled drawings of the muscles and bones of the domestic turkey, Meleagris gallopavo, an important member of the gallinaceous birds. The nomenclature as used for the muscles is based on the BNA (1920), Fisher (1955), and where no other source was available, we used terms that were as near correctly Latinized as we could make them. Determination of muscle homologies and the final names based on these for birds must await a more thorough study of muscles in other species and understanding of the embryologic origin and innervation of these. Included in this Atlas is a table of bird muscle synonymies that should be useful to the student of bird anatomy. It would be anticipated that this Atlas can become an inexpensive working copy to which additions and corrections can be easily made both on the plates and in the text.

At the beginning of these studies in 1943 at the University of California, Davis, there were few references available in which both the myology and osteology of a single species of birds was covered in a single monograph. Shufeldt (1890) has published a rather complete work on the myology of the raven and in 1913 on the skeleton of the oscellated turkey Agriocharis ocellata. Kaupp (1918) published a volume on the anatomy of the chicken (Gallus) and dealt briefly with the myology. An atlas on the osteology and myology of the chicken primarily for veterinarians has been published by Chamberlain (1938). Two significant and recent publications on bird anatomy are those of Fisher and Goodman (1955) on the myology of the whooping crane and George and Berger (1966) on the gross description of all bird muscles with particular emphasis on the myology of the Rock Dove (Columbia livia). Recognition of other essential references would be redundant since the bibliographies presented by these latter authors are extensive and complete.

In preparation of this Atlas, our particular thanks must go to Mrs. Beverly Farmer at the University of California, Davis, California, who devoted many hours to the initial drawings from dissections and to Mrs. Hazel Thelan, Vacaville, California, who did the final pen and ink drawings. Labeling of the plates of myology was done by Mrs. Elsie Froeschner, Arlington, Virginia, for which $300.00 was granted by the Research Endowment Funds of Montana State College. Several bone plates were done by Miss Anne V. Donovan, Washington, D. C., for which a grant from the Dowden Fund (No. 2) at George Washington University was used, and the final labeling of bone plates was done by Mrs. J. Switzer of Washington, D. C. Recognition must also be given to Mrs. Carol Freed who typed the manuscript in its final form for publication. Mr. and Mrs. Joseph Garibaldi, Stockton, California, must also receive thanks for their part in making available funds utilized in the overall cost leading to the preparation of this Atlas. Dr. C. L. Dunham, formerly Director of the Division of Biology and Medicine, and Dr. John Totter, Director of the Division of Biology and Medicine of the U.S. Atomic Energy Commission, through their kindness and office, made possible the final steps necessary to the publication of this Atlas. Finally, recognition must be given to Mr. Robert Pigeon, Division of Technical Information, U.S. Atomic Energy Commission, for his continual stimulation that encouraged us to complete and bring to press this publication.

LIST OF PLATES

Myology

Osteology

INTRODUCTION

"It is curious indeed how very few birds have been at all thoroughly dissected." This quote from Beddard in 1898 is as true today as it was in his time. Even though the domestic turkey has become a bird of worldwide economic importance, it has received little persistent attention from anatomists. As early as 1913, Shufeldt pointed out the differences between the skulls of the domestic turkey (<u>Meleagris gallopavo</u>) and the wild turkey (<u>Agriocharis ocellata</u>) and had earlier (1887) described the skeletal elements of this species. Nevertheless, few references can be found to the soft parts of the domestic turkey.

According to Shufeldt (1913), <u>Meleagris gallopavo domestica</u>, as he preferred to name the domestic turkey in lieu of a documented name, shows the closest relationship to <u>Gallus bankiva</u> and true fowls. In addition, the turkey skeleton, typical of the gallinaceous birds, has other characteristics that connect it with the Phasianidae, pheasant family. More recent work has not clarified the problem of properly classifying the turkey. Shorger (1967) reviews in brief the methods and conclusions of various workers in attempting to properly relate the turkey to other species of birds. Whether to "place the turkey among the pheasants or in a separate family depends on whether the approach is anatomical, physiological, morphological, or otherwise" (Shorger, 1967). Ridgway and Friedmann (1946:63, 436) placed the turkeys in the separate family Meleagridae under the superfamily Phasianoide on the basis of the head furnishings, the truncated color feathers, the acetabulu, and the weak, straight furcula. Hudson, et al, (1959:56) write that, except for the loss of the femorocaudal portion of the pyriform muscle, the turkey is essentially a pheasant. Nevertheless, the consensus of opinion holds that the turkey is a primitive member of the Galliformes.

Turkeys are clearly of North American origin, and Howard (1950) has stated that they are known with certainty only from late pliocene and early Pleistocene. However, Wetmore (1936) believes that they were common in the West during the Miocene.

The South Mexican turkey, the original Meleagris gallopavo of Linnaeus, although a domestic bird (Newton, 1868:102), must be the starting point for the various subspecies. The Mexicans domesticated the native turkey, which extended from Vera Cruz westward, and it is the domestic bird that was introduced into Europe. The wild bird, accordingly, must be <u>Meleagris gallopavo gallopavo</u>. When Gould (1856) described his Mexican turkey (<u>Meleagris mexicana</u>), he contended that Linneaus based his <u>Meleagris gallopavo</u> on the wild turkey found north of Mexico. This led to the use of <u>M</u>. <u>gallopavo</u> for the eastern turkey in the AOU Check-lists until the turn of the century. Characteristic of the native Mexican race are the white tips of the tail feathers and the upper tail coverts. Bonaparte (1825:98) used these characteristics to identify the tame turkeys sold as wild ones in the Philadelphia and New York markets. The white "rump" has been eliminated in nearly all of the modern domestic turkeys, but the white tips of the tail feathers persist. Baird (1867) stated that the domestic turkey is unquestionably of Mexican origin. Coues (1897), after discussing the nomenclature, came to a solution, that of naming the Mexican bird _Meleagris gallopavo gallopavo_.

The origin of the common and generic name of the turkey and its domestication are equally difficult to trace from the literature as are its taxonomic relationships. Shorger (1967) discusses these, and for students wishing to pursue this question further, his bibliography is extensive.

An atlas of the myology and osteology of any species does not in itself help to resolve questions of phylogenetic relationships or the history of domestication. However, if this Atlas increases interest in either of these problems or makes possible new research utilizing the turkey, it will have served its purpose.

MATERIALS AND METHODS

Twenty-five mature male and female domestic turkeys, <u>Meleagris gallopavo</u>, obtained from the poultry department at the University of California, Davis, were used in this study. Two breeds, the Broad-Breasted Bronze and White Holland turkeys, were utilized in studies of the myology and preparation of the skeletal materials. One skeleton of a three-month-old Broad-Breasted Bronze turkey was prepared for separation of the individual skull bones.

The turkeys used for dissection and muscle studies were embalmed and kept refrigerated at 4° C until needed for study.

The turkeys to be embalmed were killed with chloroform or ether. An incision was made through the skin in the caudal lateral aspect of the thigh. This exposes the caudal fan of the <u>M</u>. <u>gluteus primus</u> and <u>M</u>. <u>biceps flexor cruris</u>. These muscles can be separated from each other to the depth of the femur without tearing muscle tissue. The ischiadic nerve and artery and the vena cruralis lie deep and caudal to the femur. The ischiadic artery was lifted carefully and thread tied around the artery at its cardiac end. A canula was placed in an incision that is made in the artery and tied securely.

The embalming fluid consisted of:

Formalin	1.5 parts
Carbolic Acid	2.5 parts
Glycerine	10.0 parts
Water	86.0 parts

and was placed in a two liter perfusion bottle about four feet above the bird. This height permits adequate perfusion pressure. Perfusion was continued until the wattle became distended and the fluid leaked freely from the oronasal passages. For birds over 15 pounds, two liters of fluid is adequate, whereas, for those under 15 pounds, one to two liters are adequate. The birds were left at room temperature for 24 to 48 hours before storing in a cold room at 4°C.

Pencil drawings were made of each layer of muscles as they were exposed, the accuracy of these were confirmed or corrected from subsequent dissections and finally inked for final plates. We utilized a minimum of artistic license; therefore, the larger number of plates than usual in this type of study have permitted us to show accurately the succession of each layer of muscles.

An autoclave method was utilized in the preparation of the skeletal materials. Mature fresh male and female turkeys were eviscerated, skinned, and disjointed. The head, feet, and wings were placed in cheese cloth bags. They were placed in an autoclave for 35 minutes at 15 pounds pressure. Following this treatment, the bones were easily defleshed. To attain bones of good quality for drawings and study purposes, the defleshed bones were placed in a solution of chlorox and water (1:20). This treatment permitted removal of ligamentous materials remaining attached to the bones and also bleached them an appropriate amount.

Preparation of the skeleton in this way, when done carefully so as to avoid breaking small bones and cartilage and excessive removal of skeletal material, takes approximately eight hours.

A. Myology

Research on birds and their anatomy has not advanced at the same rate as that for other classes of vertebrates. Therefore, significant contributions to knowledge in the fields of biology must await the solution to many problems that remain unanswered for birds. Of particular note is the absence in the literature of studies on comparative myology in the birds. This is particularly noteworthy since there are in existence and readily available for research flightless birds, wild as well as domestic species, and representatives from nearly all ecosystems. We must agree with George and Berger (1966) list of four types of research needed on the avian muscular system. These are: "1) Descriptions of the complete appendicular myology of all genera in different families of birds . . .; 2) Comparison of the wing myology of flightless (or nearly flightless) genera with flying genera in the same family . . .; 3) Nerve-muscle experiments on living birds. . .; 4) Studies of the gross pattern of the brachial and lumbosacral plexuses. . . as well as nerve degeneration experiments. . ."

The turkey has been domesticated in the recent history and several wild species are both readily available and maintained easily in captivity. In addition, the turkey has gained prominence as one of the more important economic birds. For these several reasons, intensive research on turkeys would be highly rewarding.

1. Muscles of Taxonomic Significance

Use of muscles for taxonomic purposes in birds has resulted in a number of papers on specific muscle groups thought to be of significance. Little effort has been made to describe all muscles in any one species. We have not oriented this Atlas to the taxonomic significance of the turkey muscles; however, we include here a brief discussion of the muscles as we observed them in the turkey. Garrod (1873 and 1874) used a set of symbols for designation of thigh muscles that he believed were of taxonomic significance. This "set" has been modified by Hudson (1937) and is discussed in some detail by Fisher (1955) and George and Berger (1966).

Following these authors and Newton (1895) the wild turkey M. gallapavo has the formula B C D E F G X Y Am and for the domestic turkey M. g. gallapavo the same formula probably pertains according to our study. However, we did not successfully identify an M. plantaris /F_/ of George and Berger (1966).

The M. femorocaudal /‾A‾/ (=caudofemoralis) is absent in the turkey. However, the accessory part of M. femorocaudal /_B_/ (=pars iliofemoralis, = M. piriformis) or ischiofemoralis as we have preferred_to_name this muscle is present. The gluteus medius et _ minimus /_D_/ (=gluteus superficialis of our study), iliacus /_E_/, popliteus $\underline{/\,G\,/}$, semitendinosus $\underline{/\,X\,/}$, semitendinosus accessorius $\underline{/\,Y\,/}$, ambiens $\underline{/\,Am\,/}$ and viniculum $\underline{/\,V\,/}$ were all observed in our study. Although we are certain that we identified M. plantaris $\underline{/\,F\,/}$, we would prefer that this question remain to be solved without doubt through future research. George and Berger (1966) report that the tendon of this muscle is ossified in some gallinaceous birds.

Other muscles considered of taxonomic importance have been listed by Newton (1895). A brief description of these for the turkey follows (see also description of plates).

There are two pectoralis muscles in the turkey: pectoralis superficialis and pectoralis profundus. The superficial pectoral is the largest muscle of the turkey. It inserts by a broad fascia on the deltoid crest of the humerus and by a more caudal thin but tough fascia to the teres and patagialis. The pectoralis profundus on the other hand inserts on the humerus by a tendon.

The coracobrachialis (M. Supracoracoideus of Newton) inserts on the deltoid crest of the humerus after passing through the foramen triosseum. In the turkey this muscle appears to simply extend the brachium, whereas Newton states that it rotates and abducts the humerus.

The patagialis complex (M. Propatagialis longus, and Propatagialis brevis of Newton) in the turkey is composed of three distinctly different units: the patagialis, tensor patagi longus, tensor patagi caudalis. In the turkey the patagialis inserts broadly by fascia on the extensor carpi radialis superficialis and skin of the wing. The tensor patagi longus inserts on the radial carpal sesamoid that lies just distal to the radial carpal bone. A slip extends from this muscle to insert on the skin of the manus, whereas, the tensor patagi caudalis inserts on the skin of the antibrachium by fascia.

In Gallinae and Columbidae (excluding Cracidae) the propatagialis receives a slip from the biceps. We could find no trace of a slip arising from the biceps and inserting on the patagial complex.

The latissimus dorsi (Latissimus dorsi of Newton) is composed of two portions: a cranial and a caudal head. Insertion of the cranial portion is on the shaft of the humerus, and the caudal portion inserts on the cranial portion. We did not observe inserting fibers or fascia from either portion on the patagium or the anconeus longus as described for other birds.

A muscle described as the expansor secundarium of Newton was not observed in the turkey; however, Newton states that this muscle is in the Gallinae but is absent in Columbidae. It is also of poor taxonomic value according to Newton (1895).

2. Ambiens (M. Ambiens of Newton)

Though a so-called perching muscle, this is absent in many perching birds. In the domestic turkey this muscle is small, originates on the pubis, and inserts on the originating tendon of the flexor digiti terti perforatis. It, therefore, appears to aid in flexing the foot digits II, III and IV. According to Newton (1895) in most birds the M. ambiens originates on the proacetabular ilium and aids in flexion of digits II and III. In Columbae livia, the M. ambiens arises from the pubis and inserts on the M. flexores perforati digiti II, III, IV (George and Berger, 1966).

The ischiofemoralis (caudoiliofemoralis of Newton) inserts on the greater trochanter of the femur. The domestic turkey does not have an accessory (caudal part). According to Newton the accessory femoral caudal arises from the proacetabular ilium and is present in most Gallinae but absent in Pavo and Meleagris. Kaupp (1918) and Chamberlain (1938) report this muscle in the chicken.

Semitendinosus (M. Semitendinosus of Newton) in the domestic turkey originates from the caudal crest of the ilium, whereas, Newton (1895) reports that in Gallinae this muscle originates from the ilium and caudal vertebrae.

3. Semimembranosus (M. Semimembranosus of Newton) is a prominent muscle in the turkey, but Newton claims this to be much reduced in Columbae.

A further discussion of the taxonomic value of muscles in birds would serve no useful purpose here. Without additional information that can only be gotten through new studies, one cannot even be sure that he is comparing homologous muscles of one species with that described by another author.

We utilized as nearly as possible the correct Latinized form for naming of the turkey muscles. A binomial nomenclature was used wherever possible, in which the origin of the muscle was placed first and the insertion second in the binomial. The table of muscle synonomies is intended as a guide and it would be anticipated that many corrections in this table will be made before it will be completed or entirely discarded.

Plate 1   Head   Right Lateral View

Superficial and Second Layers
  1. M. articulohyoideus - (See Plate 3)
  2. M. articulomylohyoideus - (See Plate 3)
  3. M. biventer maxillae - (See Plate 2)
  4. M. complexus - (See Plate 7)
  5. M. cutaneus colli lateralis - (See Plate 7)

  6. M. depressor palpebrarum ventralis, ventral depressor of the eyelid
     (not figured)
       FORM AND RELATIONSHIPS: scanty fibers lying in fascia of ventral aspect
         of orbital fossa; under the eye and its caudal muscles; over dorsal
         palatine muscles.
       ORIGIN: palatine caudally by fibers.
       INSERTION: ventral eyelid, by fibers to fascia.
       ACTION: depresses ventral eyelid.

  7. M. geniohyoideus - (See Plate 2)
  8. M. mylohyoideus - (See Plate 3)
  9. M. quadratomandibularis - (See Plate 2)
 10. M. rectus capitis lateralis - (See Plate 9)
 11. M. sternothyrohyoideus - (See Plate 3)

 12. M. temporalis et masseter, the temporal and masseter
       FORM AND RELATIONSHIPS: slightly triangular, of three fasciculi which
         are not separable into a separate temporalis and separate masseter as
         in the chicken; just deep to zygomaticum; lies caudal to the orbit and
         cranial to the external auditory meatus; just below the skin,
         zygomatic fascia and cutaneus colli lateralis; superficial to
         mandibularis infraorbitalis, the fascia of the orbit, and to the
         mandible and zygomatic process of alisphenoid.
       ORIGIN: alisphenoid, from caudal portion of zygomatic process; also
         from temporal fossa.
       INSERTION: mandible lateral border by fibers and coronoid process
         dorsal portion by a tendon.
       ACTION: closes beak.

 13. M. trachelomastoideus - (See Plate 10)
 14. M. tracheolateralis - (See Plate 4)

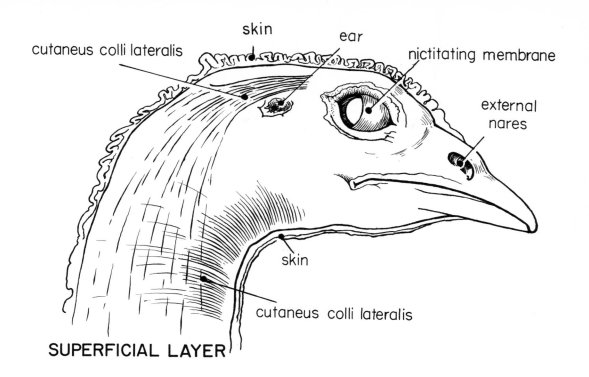

skin

cutaneus colli lateralis

ear

nictitating membrane

external nares

skin

cutaneus colli lateralis

SUPERFICIAL LAYER

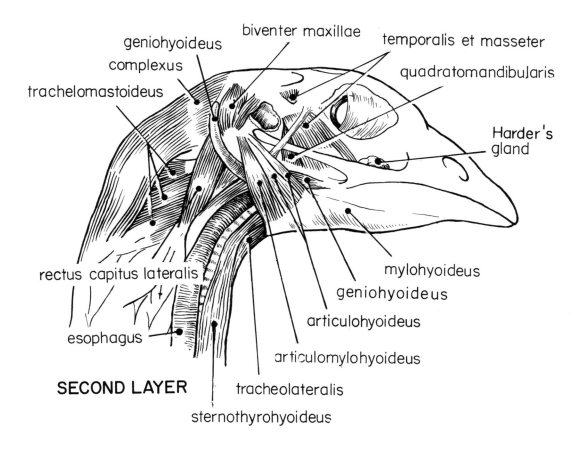

geniohyoideus

complexus

trachelomastoideus

biventer maxillae

temporalis et masseter

quadratomandibularis

Harder's gland

rectus capitus lateralis

mylohyoideus

geniohyoideus

articulohyoideus

articulomylohyoideus

esophagus

tracheolateralis

sternothyrohyoideus

SECOND LAYER

HEAD–RIGHT LATERAL VIEW
PLATE I

Plate 2   Head   Right Lateral View

Third and Deep Layers
  1. M. articulohyoideus, articulohyoid - (See Plate 3)

  2. M. biventer maxillae, the biventer of the jaw
       FORM AND RELATIONSHIPS: short, thick and triangular; follows contours
         of caudoventral angle of caudal process of the pars articularis; lies
         below cutaneous colli lateralis; above lateral portion of the
         lambdoidal suture; caudal to articulomylohyoideus and articulohyoideus;
         cranial to geniohyoideus.
       ORIGIN: lambdoidal suture, lateral surface and ridge caudal to the
         external auditory meatus by fibers.
       INSERTION: pars articularis, caudomedial surface of caudal process of
         the pars articularis of the mandible by fibers.
       ACTION: opens the beak.

  3. M. entotympanicus - (See Plate 4)

  4. M. geniohyoideus, geniohyoid
       FORM AND RELATIONSHIPS: mostly tubular, surrounding the cornu of the
         hyoid apparatus; just under the skin except where covered by
         articulohyoideus and articulomylohyoideus; caudal to biventer maxillae.
       ORIGIN: mandible, medial surface of splenial element by fibers.
       INSERTION: epibranchial of hyoid by fibers; on cutaneus colli lateralis
         by fascia.
       ACTION: pulls hyoid apparatus cranially.

  5. M. mandibularis infraorbitalis, infraorbital mandibular muscle
       FORM AND RELATIONSHIPS: short, straplike; in caudal area of orbit
         lateral to rostral process of the quadrate; under the temporalis et
         masseter laterally; superficial to the quadratomandibularis.
       ORIGIN: along the suture between alisphenoid and temporal wing of
         sphenoid medially.
       INSERTION: pars supra-angularis, to dorsal portion cranial to coronoid
         process.
       ACTION: closes beak.

  6. M. mandibulopalatinus - (See Plate 4)

  7. M. pterygomandibularis, the pterygomandibular muscle
       FORM AND RELATIONSHIPS: flat, fleshy band just ventral to cranial
         process of pterygoideus; ventral to quadratomandibularis; caudal to
         mandibulopalatinus; dorsal to medial process of pars articularis of
         mandible.
       ORIGIN: pterygoideus, dorsal surface.
       INSERTION: pars articularis, dorsal and cranial portion of medial
         process.
       ACTION: closes beak and pulls pterygoideus laterally.

  8. M. quadratomandibularis, quadratomandibular muscle
       FORM AND RELATIONSHIPS: small and thick; deep to the temporalis et
         masseter; partially covers lateral aspect of quadrate; cranial
         mandibular articulating process.
       ORIGIN: quadrate cranial process.
       INSERTION: pars supra-angularis, on lateral and medial surfaces.
       ACTION: closes beak.

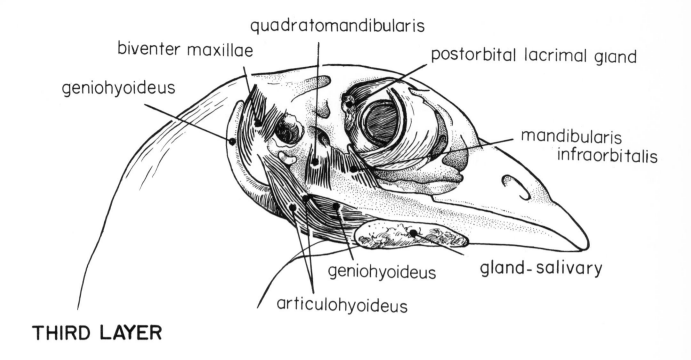

quadratomandibularis

biventer maxillae

postorbital lacrimal gland

geniohyoideus

mandibularis
infraorbitalis

geniohyoideus

gland-salivary

articulohyoideus

THIRD LAYER

DEEP LAYERS

pterygomandibularis

biventer maxillae

optic foramen

mandibulopalatinus

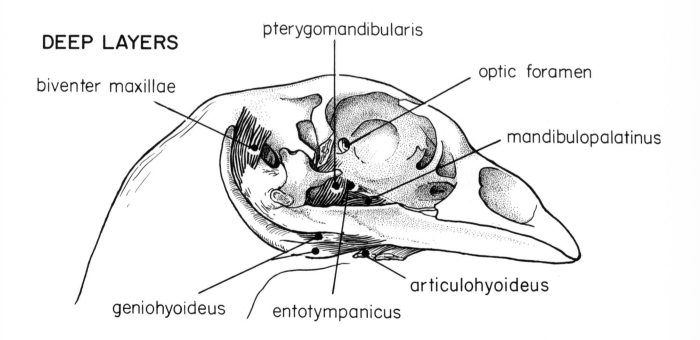

articulohyoideus

geniohyoideus

entotympanicus

**HEAD–RIGHT LATERAL VIEW
PLATE 2**

Plate 3   Head   Ventral View

Superficial and Second Layers

1. M. articulohyoideus, articulohyoid
   FORM AND RELATIONSHIPS: flat, bipartite, V-shaped; under the
      mylohyoideus and basientoglossus, superficial to the sterno-
      thyrohyoideus and geniohyoideus, anterior to the biventer maxillae
      and articulomylohyoideus; one band of muscle extends medially to hyoid
      and one cranially to lateral surface of entoglossum.
   ORIGIN: pars articularis, caudal process by fibers.
   INSERTION: (a) caudal slip--on basibranchial.
               (b) cranial slip--on basihyal.
   ACTION: suspends and raises hyoid apparatus.

2. M. articulomylohyoideus
   FORM AND RELATIONSHIPS: thin band just below the skin; caudal to
      articulohyoideus; superficial to geniohyoideus.
   ORIGIN: pars articularis, caudal process between origin of
      articulohyoideus and insertion of biventer maxillae by fibers.
   INSERTION: on mylohyoideus at caudal limit of its median raphe.
   ACTION: aids in suspending hyoid apparatus.

3. M. geniohyoideus, geniohyoid - (See Plate 2)

4. M. mylohyoideus, mylohyoid
   FORM AND RELATIONSHIPS: broad and flat covering area between mandibles;
      just under the skin; superficial to articulohyoideus and depressor
      glossi; anterior to articulomylohyoideus.
   ORIGIN: mandible, medial surface.
   INSERTION: the mylohyoideus of right and left side unite in a median
      raphe.
   ACTION: suspends and raises hyoid apparatus.

5. M. sternothyrohyoideus, sternothyroid muscle
   FORM AND RELATIONSHIPS: most superficial of the tracheal group of
      muscles; long and ribbonlike extending the length of the neck;
      just under skin; under the articulomylohyoideus cranially, over
      tracheolateralis.
   ORIGIN: cranial thoracic air sac, by fibers; skin, by fascia.
   INSERTION: cricoid cartilage and arytenohyoids by fasiculae.
   ACTION: pulls larynx caudally.

6. M. tracheolateralis, lateral muscle of the trachea - (See Plate 4)

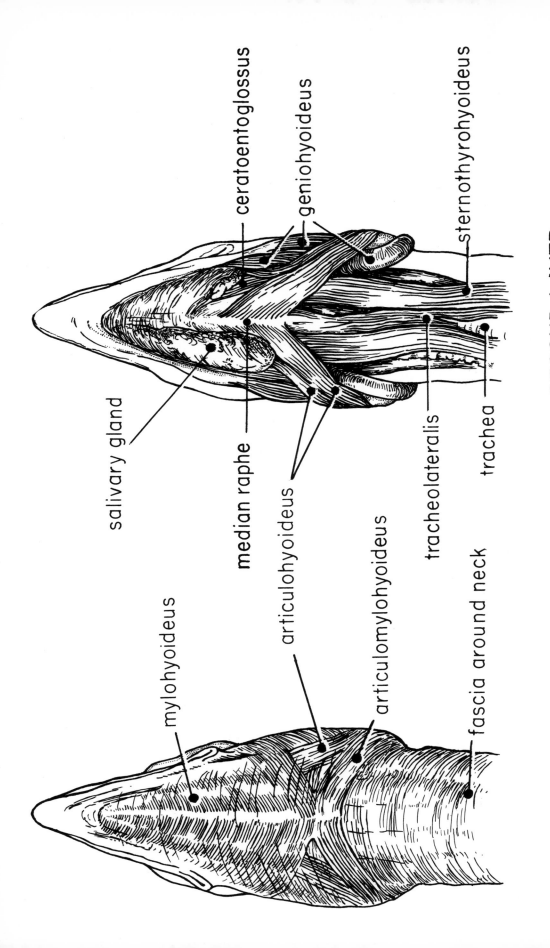

ceratoentoglossus

geniohyoideus

sternothyrohyoideus

salivary gland

median raphe

articulohyoideus

articulomylohyoideus

tracheolateralis

trachea

mylohyoideus

fascia around neck

SECOND LAYER

SUPERFICIAL LAYER

HEAD – VENTRAL VIEW
PLATE 3

Plate 4   Head and Glossus   Ventral View

Third and Fourth Layers
1. M. biventer maxillae, the biventer of the jaw - (See Plate 2)

2. M. ceratoentoglossus, ceratoentoglossal muscle
   FORM AND RELATIONSHIPS: a small band; under the submaxillary salivary
      glands and geniohyoideus; superficial to basientoglossus; lateral to
      depressor glossi.
   ORIGIN: hyoid ceratobranchial element, from lateral border.
   INSERTION: entoglossum, ventral surface.
   ACTION: depresses tip of tongue.

3. M. entotympanicus, the entotympanic muscle
   FORM AND RELATIONSHIPS: short, broad and flat; cranial to basisphenoid;
      caudal to quadratum, dorsal to pterygoideum.
   ORIGIN: basisphenoid, cranial portion by fibers.
   INSERTION: quadratum ventral process on mediocaudal surface.
   ACTION: aids in maintaining position of mandibula.

4. M. geniohyoideus, geniohyoid - (See Plate 2)

5. M. hyoideus transversus, transverse hyoid muscle
   FORM AND RELATIONSHIPS: broad band, within right and left cornua of
      hyoid; deeper than the geniohyoideus but superficial to basibranchial
      element.
   ORIGIN: basibranchial, lateral border.
   INSERTION: ceratobranchial, medial border.
   ACTION: aids closure of larynx by drawing ceratobranchials medially.

6. M. mandibulopalatinus, the mandibulopalatine muscle
   FORM AND RELATIONSHIPS: small, slightly triangular; just dorsal to skin
      of soft palate; ventral to orbital fossa; cranial to pterygomandibu-
      laris.
   ORIGIN: pars articularis, medial to the coronoid process.
   INSERTION: palatine, along lateral border of caudal articulating process
      by fibers.
   ACTION: pulls palatine laterally and ventrally.

7. M. sternothyrohyoideus, sternothyroid muscle - (See Plate 3)
8. M. temporalis et masseter, the temporal and masseter - (See Plate 1)

9. M. tracheolateralis, lateral muscle of the trachea
   FORM AND RELATIONSHIPS: long delicate muscle laterally on most of
      trachea.
   ORIGIN: trachea laterally about one-fourth the distance cranially from
      the bronchi by fibers.
   INSERTION: trachea ventrally; just caudal to superior larynx by fibers.
   ACTION: shortens trachea.

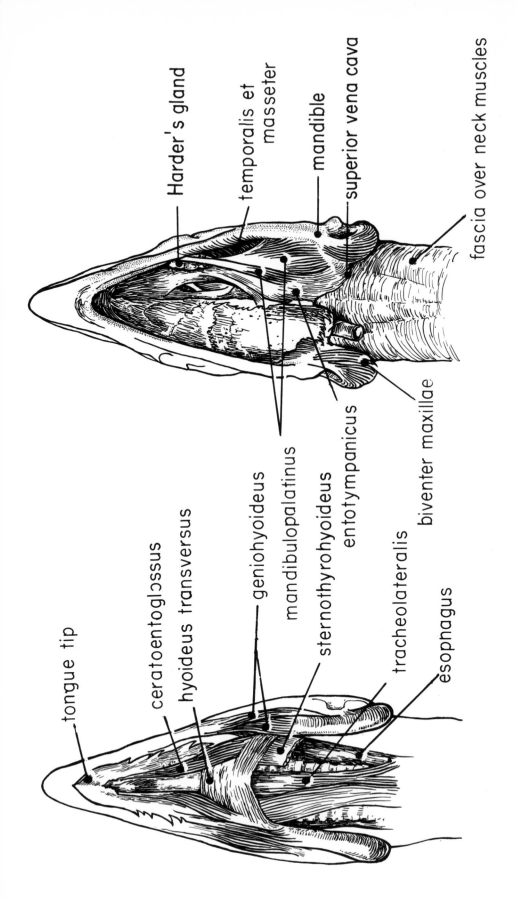

GLOSSUS–THIRD LAYER

tongue tip

ceratoentoglossus

hyoideus transversus

geniohyoideus

mandibulopalatinus

sternothyrohyoideus

entotympanicus

tracheolateralis

biventer maxillae

esophagus

Harder's gland

temporalis et masseter

mandible

superior vena cava

fascia over neck muscles

HEAD–FOURTH LAYER

HEAD AND GLOSSUS – VENTRAL VIEW
PLATE 4

Plate 5   Head and Glossus   Ventral View

Fifth and Deep Layers

1. M. basientoglossus, basientoglossal muscle
   FORM AND RELATIONSHIPS: a small band; under ceratoentoglossus;
      superficial to cranial slip of articulohyoideus.
   ORIGIN: basihyal, craniolateral surface.
   INSERTION: entoglossum, caudolateral process medial surface.
   ACTION: depresses tongue.

2. M. depressor glossi, depressor of the tongue
   FORM AND RELATIONSHIPS: quite small and thick; just below the
      mylohyoideus; medial to ceratoentoglossus.
   ORIGIN: basihyal, cranioventral surface.
   INSERTION: entoglossum tip, ventrally.
   ACTION: depresses the tongue.

3. M. thyrobasihyal, thyrobasihyal muscle
   FORM AND RELATIONSHIPS: short and broad; dorsal to basibranchial,
      basihyal, certobranchial and the hyoideus transversus; the
      thyrobasihyals of each side meet medially just superficial to the
      laryngeal cartilage.
   ORIGIN: thyroid cartilage, from lateral and ventral surfaces.
   INSERTION: basihyal, on dorsal surface.
   ACTION: elevates the tongue when the thyrobasihyals of each side work
      together; deflects tongue laterally when these act individually; aids
      in pulling larynx cranially.

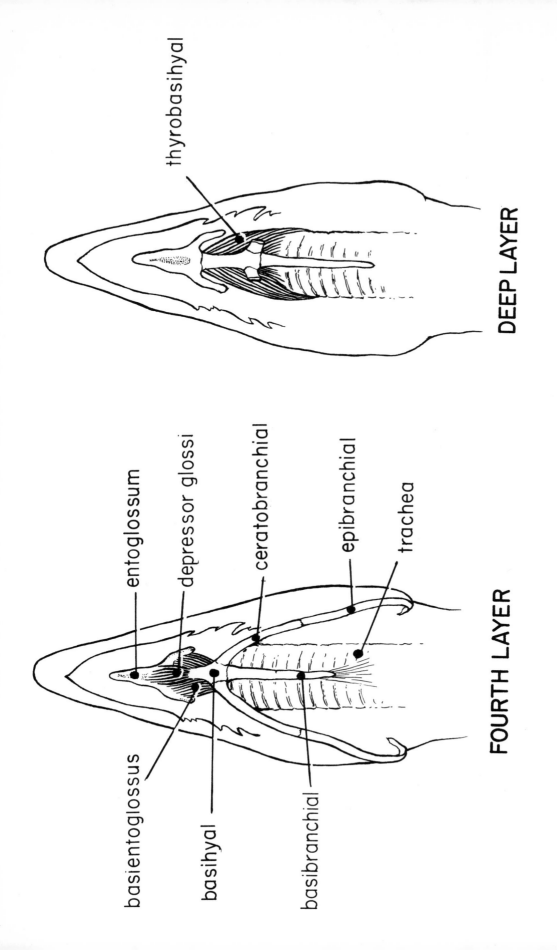

thyrobasihyal

DEEP LAYER

entoglossum

depressor glossi

ceratobranchial

epibranchial

trachea

basientoglossus

basihyal

basibranchial

FOURTH LAYER

HEAD AND GLOSSUS, VENTRAL VIEW
PLATE 5

Plate 6   Eye   Right

First and Second and Deep Layers

1. M. obliquus oculi dorsalis, dorsal oblique muscle of the eye
   FORM AND RELATIONSHIPS: triangular; on dorsal surface of eye; lies over
   the quadratus oculi and under the rectus oculi dorsalis.
   ORIGIN: orbital fundus, from dorsocranial angle.
   INSERTION: sclera, dorsally.
   ACTION: rolls the eye dorsally and slightly caudally.

2. M. obliquus oculi ventralis, ventral oblique muscle of the eye
   FORM AND RELATIONSHIPS: narrow flat band in cranioventral region of the
   eye; lies over pyramidalis oculi, Harder's gland and sclera; cranio-
   medial to rectus oculi cranialis.
   ORIGIN: orbital fundus, just cranial to origin of obliquus oculi
   dorsalis by fibers.
   INSERTION: sclera, ventrally by fibers.
   ACTION: rolls the eye cranially.

3. M. pyramidalis oculi, pyramidalis muscle of the eye
   FORM AND RELATIONSHIPS: flat, triangular; on sclera of eye just
   anterior to optic nerve; tendon of the muscle lies in a sling formed
   by the quadratus oculi.
   ORIGIN: sclera, from an area just anterior to optic nerve and at
   insertion of rectus oculi ventralis.
   INSERTION: nictitating membrane on caudal free border by a tendon.
   ACTION: draws nictitating membrane across the eye; may work
   independently of other eye movements.

4. M. quadratus oculi, quadrate muscle of the eye
   FORM AND RELATIONSHIPS: broad and flat; composed of three fasciculi;
   lies dorsally and medially over the sclera; under the rectus oculi
   dorsalis, rectus oculi caudalis, rectus oculi cranialis, and obliquus
   oculi dorsalis; forms a sling for tendon of pyramidalis oculi.
   ORIGIN: sclera, dorsal quadrant of eye.
   INSERTION: sclera, just dorsal to optic nerve.
   ACTION: acts as a moveable pulley for tendon of pyramidalis oculi.

5. M. rectus oculi caudalis, caudal rectus muscle of the eye
   FORM AND RELATIONSHIPS: broad and flat; in caudal area of eye;
   anterior to caudal face of orbital plate of frontal bone.
   ORIGIN: alisphenoid.
   INSERTION: sclera, caudomedially.
   ACTION: rolls eye craniomedially.

6. M. rectus oculi cranialis, cranial rectus muscle of the eye.
   FORM AND RELATIONSHIPS: broad, triangular and flat; superficial to
   sclera and quadratus oculi.
   ORIGIN: interorbital plate dorsal to optic foramen by fibers.
   INSERTION: sclera, cranial portion of the eye by fibers.
   ACTION: rolls the eye cranially.

7. M. rectus oculi dorsalis, dorsal rectus muscle of the eye
   FORM AND RELATIONSHIPS: triangular; dorsocaudally on eye.
   ORIGIN: orbital plate, just caudal to optic foramen by a tendon.
   INSERTION: sclera superficially to insertion of obliquus oculi dorsalis
   by loose fascia.
   ACTION: rolls eye dorsocaudally.

8. M. rectus oculi ventralis, ventral rectus of the eye
    FORM AND RELATIONSHIPS: flat band in caudoventral region of eye; lies
        over pyramidalis oculi, under Harder's gland.
    ORIGIN: orbital fundus ventral to optic foramen by fibers.
    INSERTION: sclera, ventral surface of the eye by fibers.
    ACTION: rolls the eye ventrally.

FIRST LAYER

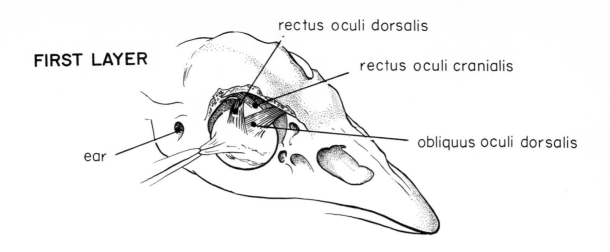

rectus oculi dorsalis

rectus oculi cranialis

obliquus oculi dorsalis

ear

SECOND LAYER

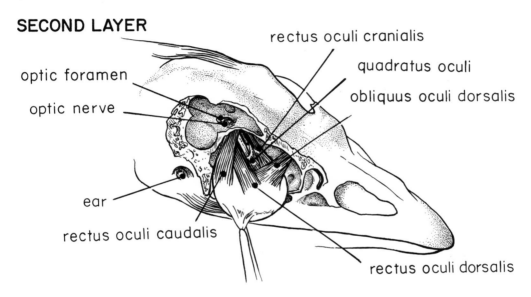

rectus oculi cranialis

quadratus oculi

obliquus oculi dorsalis

optic foramen

optic nerve

ear

rectus oculi caudalis

rectus oculi dorsalis

DEEP LAYERS

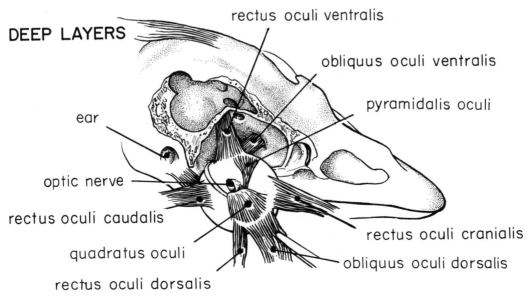

rectus oculi ventralis

obliquus oculi ventralis

pyramidalis oculi

ear

optic nerve

rectus oculi caudalis

quadratus oculi

rectus oculi dorsalis

rectus oculi cranialis

obliquus oculi dorsalis

EYE-RIGHT   PLATE 6

Plate 7   Neck   Dorsal View

Superficial Layer

1. M. biventer cervicis, two-bellied cervical muscle
    FORM AND RELATIONSHIPS: long, thin and tapering to head; most dorsal
      and medial of neck muscles; under the complexus cranially, but other-
      wise just under the skin; over the longus colli dorsalis and rectus
      capitis dorsalis; tendinous at origin, becoming fleshy about three-
      fourths caudally on neck, then tendinous again at about one-half
      caudally on neck and fleshy again in region of atlas.
    ORIGIN: thoracic vertebrae one and two, dorsal spines by aponeurosis
      (tendon-like) in common with tendon of longus colli dorsalis.
    INSERTION: occipital crest, medially by fibers.
    ACTION: elevation of head and accentuation of sigmoid curve of neck.

2. M. complexus, complex muscle
    FORM AND RELATIONSHIPS: flat and wide; broadening from origin to give
      a triangular shape; most dorsal and cranial of the neck muscles; under
      cutaneus colli lateralis; over and dorsal to trachelomastoideus.
    ORIGIN: cervical vertebrae one, three and four (prezygapophyses) by
      fascia and fibers.
    INSERTION: occipital crest, dorsally, by fascia.
    ACTION: dorsal flexion of the head.

3. M. cutaneus cleidodorsalis, cleidodorsal cutaneous muscle
    FORM AND RELATIONSHIPS: narrow and flat; just under the skin; over the
      neck muscles in region of cervical vertebrae thirteen and fourteen.
    ORIGIN: from fascia in ventrocranial omobrachial region.
    INSERTION: spinal pteryla dorsal to fourteenth cervical vertebrae, by
      fibers in common with inserting fibers of cutaneus spinalis dorsalis.
    ACTION: works with cutaneus spinalis dorsalis to elevate feathers of
      the spinal pteryla.

4. M. cutaneus colli lateralis, lateral cutaneous muscle of the neck
    FORM AND RELATIONSHIPS: sheet-like, with scanty fibers; forms sheath
      over muscles of neck, trachea and esophagus.
    ORIGIN: petrous temporal, from caudal border of the external auditory
      meatus.
    INSERTION: skin of neck laterally and ventrally to level of about the
      twelfth cervical vertebra.
    ACTION: elevates cervical feathers of the spinal pteryla with cutaneous
      nuchalis.

5. M. cutaneus nuchalis, nuchal cutaneous muscle
    FORM AND RELATIONSHIPS: six ribbon-like fasciculi in middle two-thirds
      of neck; under cutaneus colli lateralis and sternothyroideus; the
      superficial neck muscles.
    ORIGIN: fascia surrounding superficial neck muscles, by fibers which
      originate ventromedially.
    INSERTION: spinal pteryla in cervical region, by fibers continuous
      with inserting fibers of cutaneus colli lateralis.
    ACTION: works with cutaneus colli lateralis to elevate cervical feathers
      of spinal pteryla.

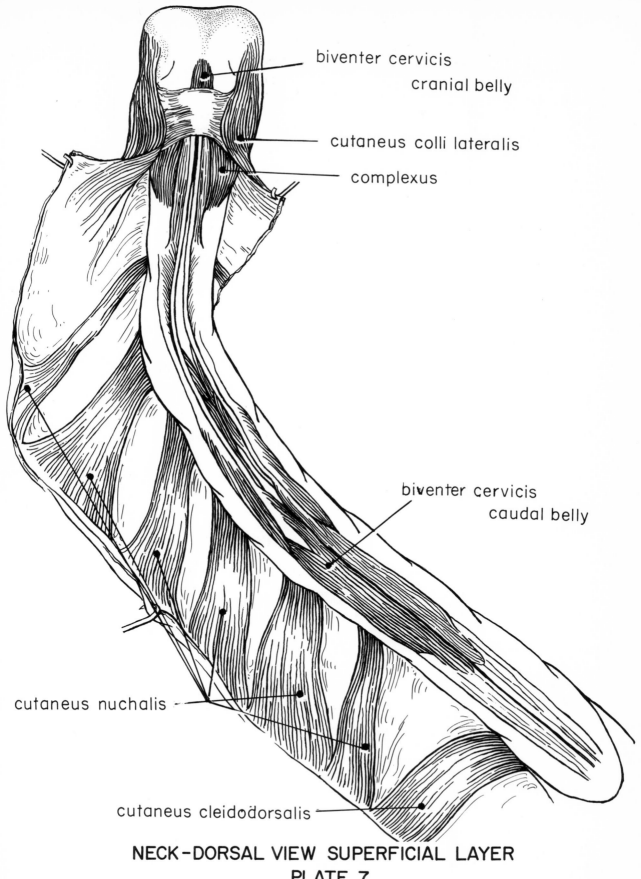

biventer cervicis
cranial belly

cutaneus colli lateralis

complexus

biventer cervicis
caudal belly

cutaneus nuchalis

cutaneus cleidodorsalis

NECK-DORSAL VIEW SUPERFICIAL LAYER
PLATE 7

Plate 8   Neck   Dorsal View

<u>First Layer</u>
1. <u>M</u>. <u>biventer</u> <u>cervicis</u>, caudal and cranial belly - (See Plate 7)

2. <u>M</u>. <u>interspinales</u> <u>craniales</u>, cranial interspinales, three in number
   FORM AND RELATIONSHIPS: ribbon-like; lateral to posterior part of <u>longus</u> <u>colli</u> <u>dorsalis</u>; dorsomedial to <u>obliqui</u> <u>colli</u>; over the <u>obliquotransversales</u> and interspinous ligaments.
   ORIGIN: cervical vertebrae ten, eleven and twelve, cranial surface of spinous processes by fibers.
   INSERTIONS: cervical vertebrae eight, nine, and ten, spinous processes dorsocaudally by fibers.
   ACTION: assists in elevation of the neck.

3. <u>M</u>. <u>longus</u> <u>colli</u> <u>dorsalis</u>, the long muscle of the neck
   FORM AND RELATIONSHIPS: long, thin multi-fasciculated muscle dorsal on neck; under the skin and <u>biventer</u> <u>cervicis</u>; over the cervical and first two thoracic vertebrae; dorsal to <u>obliqui</u> <u>colli</u>.
   ORIGIN: thoracic vertebrae one and two dorsal spines in common with <u>biventer</u> <u>cervicis</u>.
   INSERTIONS: postzygapophyses, dorsocaudally; seven ribbon-like fasciculi extend cranially to insert on fourteenth to seventh cervical vertebrae; main muscle becomes tendinous at level of seventh cervical vertebra and then gives off six more broad, ribbon-like fasciculi which extend caudally to insert on the eighth to third cervical vertebrae; terminal tendon inserts on axis.
   ACTION: cranially directed fasciculi elevate neck; caudally directed fasciculi aid in elevating head.

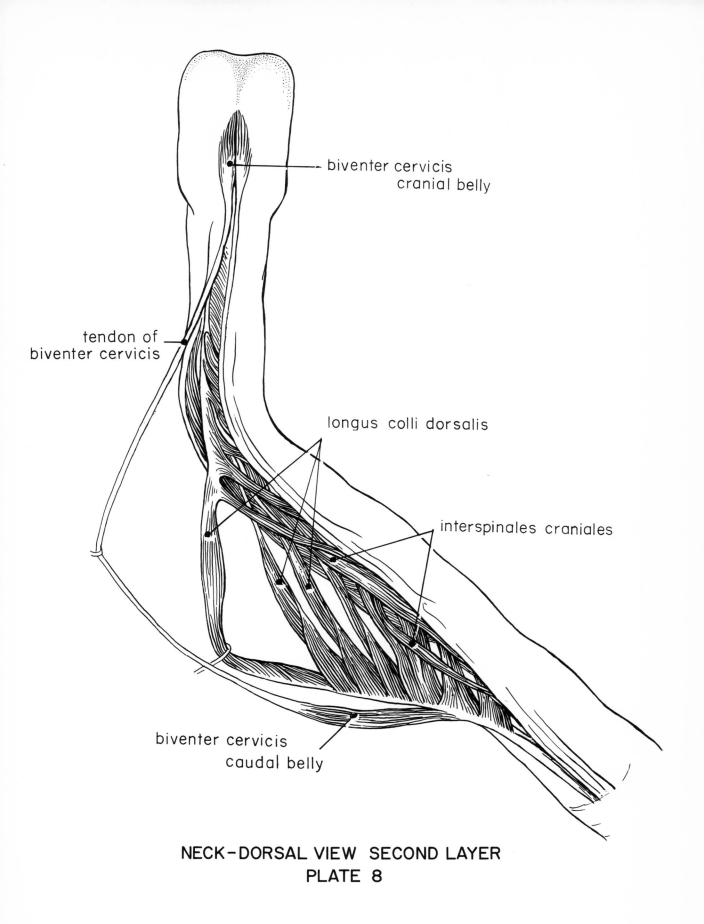

biventer cervicis
cranial belly

tendon of
biventer cervicis

longus colli dorsalis

interspinales craniales

biventer cervicis
caudal belly

NECK–DORSAL VIEW SECOND LAYER
PLATE 8

Plate 9   Neck   Lateral View

Superficial Layer
1. M. articulomylohyoideus - (See Plate 3)
2. M. biventer maxillae - (See Plate 2)
3. M. complexus - (See Plate 7)
4. M. geniohyoideus - (See Plate 2)
5. M. interspinales craniales - (See Plate 8)
6. M. intertransversales - (See Plate 10)

7. M. longi colli, the long neck muscles - (See Also Plate 13)
   This is a complex group of interrelated muscles on the superficial and ventral aspect of the neck. For convenience, the group is subdivided into three groups of fasciculi and each is considered separately.

8. M. longissimus dorsi - (See Plate 15)
9. M. longus colli dorsalis - (See Plate 8)
10. M. longus colli ventralis caudalis - (See Plate 13)
11. M. longus colli ventralis cranialis - (See Plate 13)
12. M. longus colli ventralis medialis - (See Plate 13)

13. M. obliqui colli, the lateral oblique muscles of the neck
   FORM AND RELATIONSHIPS: a complex group of ten slender muscles lateral and superficial on neck from region of third cervical to second thoracic vertebra; just deep to the skin, cutaneus nuchalis and fascia of cutaneus colli lateralis; dorsal to intertransversales interarticulares and obliquotransversales.
   ORIGINS: all arise by fibers laterally on the transverse processes of vertebrae:
      1. sixth cervical vertebra
      2. seventh cervical vertebra
      3. eighth cervical vertebra
      4. ninth cervical vertebra
      5. tenth cervical vertebra
      6. eleventh cervical vertebra
      7. fourteenth cervical vertebra, three fasciculi
      8. first thoracic vertebra
      9. second thoracic vertebra
      10. second thoracic vertebra, in common with No. 9.
   INSERTIONS: all insert by tendons dorsocaudally on postzygapophyses of vertebrae:
      1. third cervical vertebra
      2. on fifth cervical vertebra after receiving tendon of a fasciculus of longus colli dorsalis
      3. on sixth cervical vertebra after receiving tendon of a fasciculus of longus colli dorsalis
      4. on seventh cervical vertebra after receiving tendon of a fasciculus of longus colli dorsalis
      5. on eighth cervical vertebra after receiving fibers from No. 6 of the obliqui colli
      6. on eighth cervical vertebra with No. 5
      7. two fasciculi insert on the tenth cervical vertebra; one fasciculus on the eleventh cervical vertebra
      8. thirteenth cervical vertebra
      9 & 10. in common on the fourteenth cervical vertebra.
   ACTION: lateral movement of neck or dorsal flexion if all ten pairs contract simultaneously.

14. M. rectus capitis lateralis, lateral rectus of the head
    FORM AND RELATIONSHIPS: flat and triangular; deep to the cutaneous
        colli lateralis; ventral to complexus and trachelomastoideus; dorsal
        to rectus capitis ventralis.
    ORIGIN: cervical vertebrae three and four, ventral spines, by fibers.
    INSERTION: occipital crest, by fascia in common with that of complexus.
    ACTION: ventrolateral flexion of head.

15. M. rectus capitis ventralis, ventral rectus of the head
    FORM AND RELATIONSHIPS: long and triangular, dorsal to esophagus in
        region of first four cervical vertebrae; under cutaneus colli
        lateralis; ventral to rectus capitis lateralis and basitemporal plate.
    ORIGIN: third to sixth cervical vertebrae, by fibers ventrally from
        the centra.
    INSERTION: basitemporal plate, by fibers.
    ACTION: ventral flexion of the head.

16. M. sacrolumbalis - (See Plate 14)
17. M. scalenius - (See Plate 25)
18. M. tendon biventer cervicis - (See Plate 7)
19. M. trachelomastoideus - (See Plate 10)

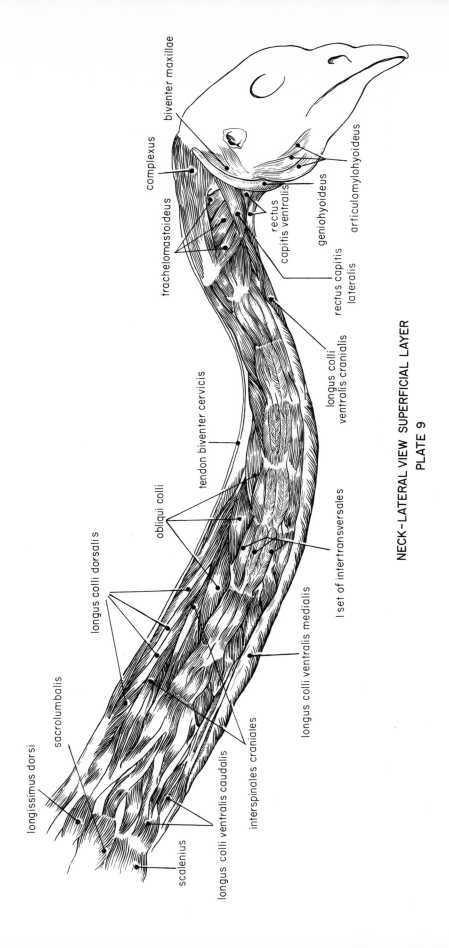

biventer maxillae

complexus

trachelomastoideus

rectus
capitis ventralis

geniohyoideus

articulomylohyoideus

rectus capitis
lateralis

longus colli
ventralis cranialis

tendon biventer cervicis

obliqui colli

longus colli
dorsalis

I set of intertransversales

sacrolumbalis

longissimus dorsi

longus colli ventralis medialis

longus colli ventralis caudalis

interspinales craniales

scalenius

NECK–LATERAL VIEW SUPERFICIAL LAYER
PLATE 9

Plate 10   Neck   Lateral View

Second Layer
  1. M. biventer cervicis - (See Plate 7)
  2. M. complexus - (See Plate 7)
  3. M. interspinales craniales - (See Plate 8)

  4. M. intertransversales, intertransversus muscles of the neck
       FORM AND RELATIONSHIPS: a group of short straplike fasciculi inti-
         mately bound to one another; between cervical vertebrae two and three,
         through thirteen and fourteen; under cutaneus colli lateralis; lateral
         to obliquotransversales; dorsal to longi colli ventrales.
       ORIGIN: cervical vertebrae three to fourteen fused diapophysis-
         parapophysis laterally by fibers.
       INSERTION: cervical vertebrae two to thirteen neurapophysis and fused
         parapophysis.
       ACTION: lateral flexion of neck.

  5. M. longus colli dorsalis - (See Plate 8)
  6. M. longus colli ventralis caudalis - (See Plate 13)
  7. M. longus colli ventralis cranialis - (See Plate 13)
  8. M. longus colli ventralis medialis - (See Plate 13)
  9. M. obliquotransversales - (See Plate 11)

 10. M. obliquus capitis caudalis, caudal oblique muscle of the head
       FORM AND RELATIONSHIPS: short, thick, double; under trachelomastoideus,
         complexus and rectus capitis dorsalis; over the interarticulares
         between axis and atlas.
       ORIGIN: fourth cervical vertebra, laterally from alar process by
         fibers; second cervical vertebra, prezygapophysis and postzygapophysis
         by fibers.
       INSERTION: atlas, lateral aspect of caudal articulating surface by
         fibers.
       ACTION: dorsal flexion of head.

 11. M. rectus capitis dorsalis - (See Plate 11)

 12. M. trachelomastoideus, trachelomastoid muscle
       FORM AND RELATIONSHIPS: well-developed muscle with three fasciculi;
         separate origins; common insertion; lateral on neck in region of first
         four cervical vertebrae; under the rectus capitis dorsalis and
         complexus; over the obliqui capitis caudales; dorsal to rectus capitis
         lateralis.
       ORIGIN: (a) cranial fasciculus--postzygapophysis of axis dorsal surface
         by fibers.
               (b) middle fasciculus--postzygapophysis of third cervical
         vertebra, lateral surface by fibers.
               (c) caudal fasciculus--postzygapophysis of fourth cervical
         vertebra, lateral surface by fibers.
       INSERTION: basitemporal plate of skull, caudal tubercle by fibers.
       ACTION: ventral flexion of the head and neck.

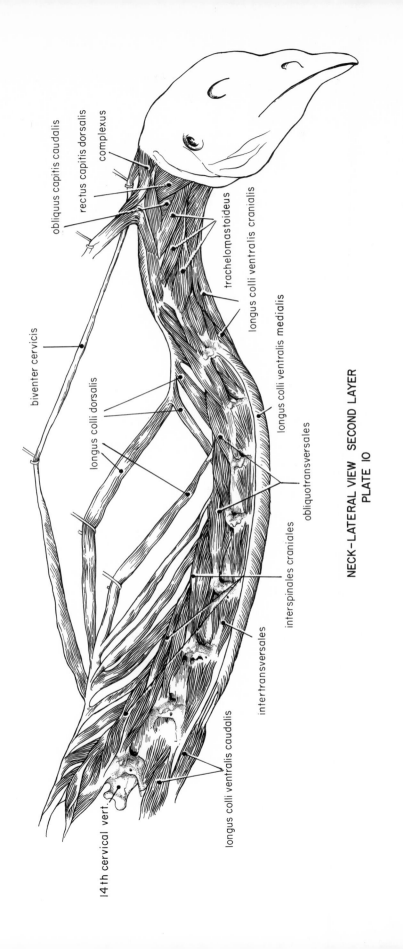

obliquus capitis caudalis

rectus capitis dorsalis

complexus

trachelomastoideus

longus colli ventralis cranialis

longus colli ventralis medialis

biventer cervicis

longus colli dorsalis

obliquotransversales

interspinales craniales

intertransversales

longus colli ventralis caudalis

14th cervical vert.

NECK–LATERAL VIEW   SECOND LAYER
PLATE 10

Plate 11   Neck   Lateral View

Third Layer
  1. M. biventer cervicis - (See Plate 7)

  2. M. interarticulares, interarticular muscles; eleven in number
      FORM AND RELATIONSHIPS: deepest muscles of the neck; broad bands
        between the cervical vertebrae beginning with second and third; lie
        under the obliquotransversales and obliquospinales.
      ORIGIN: cervical vertebrae neural arches dorsolaterally just cranial
        to anapophyses by fibers.
      INSERTION: anapophyses of preceding vertebrae caudally.
      ACTION: lateral flexion of the neck.

  3. M. longus colli dorsalis - (See Plate 8)
  4. M. longus colli ventralis cranialis - (See Plate 13)
  5. M. longus colli ventralis medialis - (See Plate 13)

  6. M. obliquospinales, oblique muscle of the neck
      FORM AND RELATIONSHIPS: three ribbon-like muscles in region of seventh
        to eleventh cervical vertebrae; under longus colli dorsalis; over
        and medial to interarticulares.
      ORIGIN: cervical vertebrae nine, ten and eleven, spinous processes
        craniolaterally by fibers.
      INSERTION: cervical vertebrae seven, eight and nine, to neural arches
        dorsocaudal aspect by fibers.
      ACTION: aid in dorsal flexure of the neck.

  7. M. obliquotransversales, oblique muscles of the neck
      FORM AND RELATIONSHIPS: short, vermiform bands just under the obliqui
        colli and with some fibers inserting in obliqui colli; over the
        cervical vertebrae; dorsomedial to interarticulares.
      ORIGIN: cervical vertebrae seven through fourteen, prezygapophyses
        laterocranially by fibers.
      INSERTION: cervical vertebrae five through twelve, postzygapophyses
        dorsal surfaces and spinous processes lateral surfaces by fibers.
      ACTION: dorsal flexion of neck and maintenance of neck curvature.

  8. M. obliquus capitis caudalis - (See Plate 10)

  9. M. rectus capitis dorsalis, dorsal rectus of the head
      FORM AND RELATIONSHIPS: short, thick and triangular; dorsal to atlas,
        axis and obliqui capitis caudales; below the complexus and biventer
        cervicis.
      ORIGIN: axis, dorsal process by fibers.
      INSERTION: occipital bone, dorsally and laterally around foramen
        magnum by fibers.
      ACTION: dorsal flexion of head.

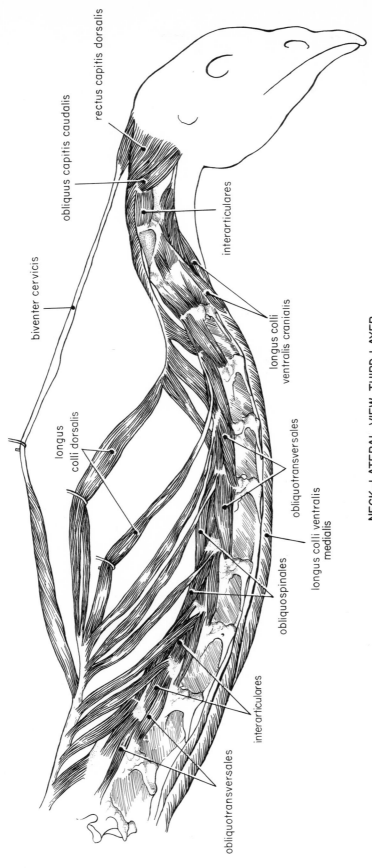

rectus capitis dorsalis

obliquus capitis caudalis

interarticulares

biventer cervicis

longus colli
ventralis cranialis

longus
colli dorsalis

obliquotransversales

longus colli ventralis
medialis

obliquospinales

interarticulares

obliquotransversales

NECK-LATERAL VIEW THIRD LAYER
PLATE II

Plate 12   Neck   Ventral View

Superficial Layer
  1. <u>M</u>. <u>cutaneus</u> <u>nuchalis</u> - (See Plate 7)
  2. <u>M</u>. <u>pectoralis</u> <u>superficialis</u> - (See Plate 20)

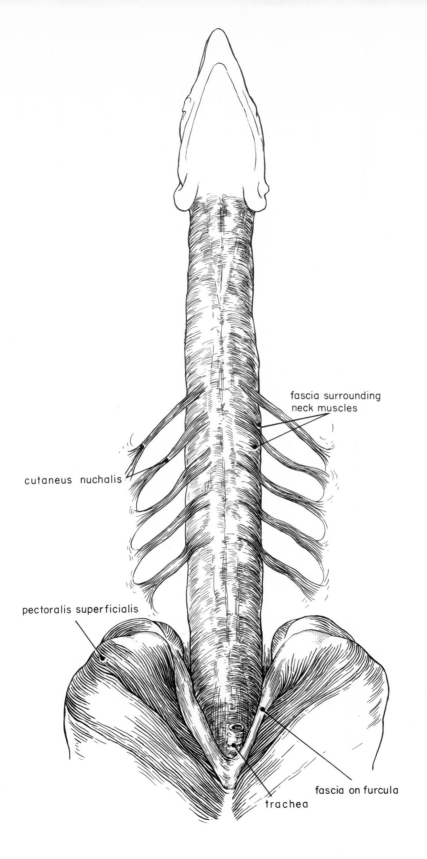

fascia surrounding
neck muscles

cutaneus nuchalis

pectoralis superficialis

fascia on furcula

trachea

NECK-VENTRAL VIEW SUPERFICIAL LAYER
PLATE 12

Plate 13   Neck   Ventral View

Second and Third Layers
1. M. complexus - (See Plate 7)
2. M. longus colli ventrales - (See Plate 9)

3. M. longus colli ventralis caudalis, long caudoventral neck muscles
   FORM AND RELATIONSHIPS: five straplike fasciculi; just under the pleural
     peritoneum in region of the crop.
   ORIGIN: thoracic vertebrae two, three and four; fused hypapophyses
     laterally, by fibers.
   INSERTION: cervical vertebrae ten through fourteen cervical ribs, by
     tendons. A small group of fibers inserts in common with each of the
     inserting tendons (these accessory fibers originate on the centra of
     the vertebrae to which the tendons insert).
   ACTION: ventral flexion at base of neck.

4. M. longus colli ventralis cranialis, long cranioventral neck muscles
   FORM AND RELATIONSHIPS: a complex mass of loosely connected fasciculi;
     under trachelomastoideus and rectus capitis ventralis; over cervical
     vertebrae two through five.
   ORIGIN: cervical vertebra five, from hypapophysis, by a tendon and
     fibers; and cervical vertebra four, by fibers from hypapophysis.
   INSERTION: cervical vertebrae two, three and four; centra and
     hypapophyses, by fibers.
   ACTION: ventral flexion of head and neck.

5. M. longus colli ventralis medialis, long medioventral neck muscles
   FORM AND RELATIONSHIPS: five long fused fasciculi; just under the skin;
     over the cervical vertebrae.
   ORIGIN: cervical vertebrae thirteen and fourteen and the first thoracic
     vertebra, parapophyses, broadly by muscle. The fasciculi extend
     cranially and terminate in five inserting tendons:
   INSERTIONS: 1. the most lateral fasciculus inserts by a tendon to the
     cervical rib of cervical vertebra ten (two small accessory fasciculi
     originate from centra of cervical vertebrae eleven and twelve and
     fuse with the main fasciculus)
           2. the next fasciculus medially, inserts on the cervical
     rib of cervical vertebrae nine (two small accessory fasciculi from
     centra of cervical vertebrae ten and eleven join with the main
     fasciculus)
           3. the middle fasciculus inserts on cervical rib of
     cervical vertebra eight (there are three small accessory fasciculi
     from centra of cervical vertebrae nine and ten and from parapophysis
     of cervical vertebra twelve)
           4. the fourth fasciculus inserts on cervical rib of
     cervical vertebra seven after having received three small accessory
     fasciculi (these originate from centra of cervical vertebrae eight
     and nine and from parapophysis of eleven)
           5. the most medial fasciculus has two inserting tendons--
     one inserts on the cervical rib of cervical vertebra six after
     receiving five accessory fasciculi from seventh through eleventh
     cervical vertebrae. The second main inserting tendon terminates on
     the cervical rib of cervical vertebra five.
   ACTION: ventral flexion of neck and reduction of its sigmoid curve.

6. M. trachelomastoideus - (See Plate 10)

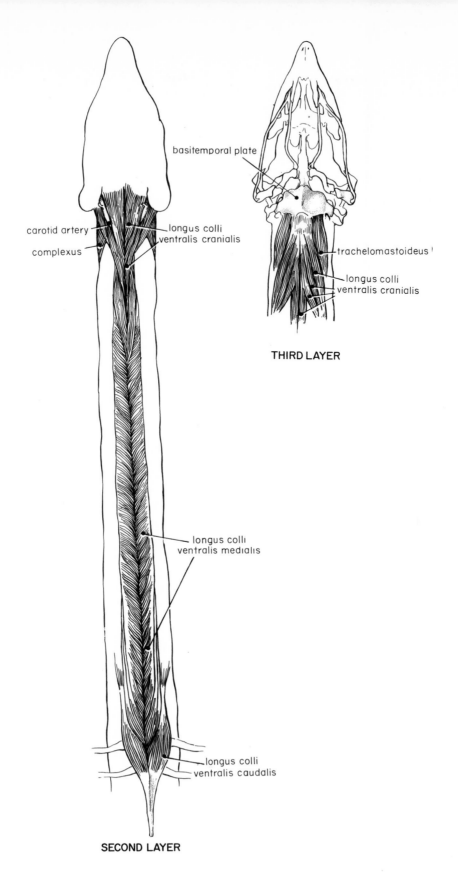

basitemporal plate

carotid artery

longus colli
ventralis cranialis

complexus

trachelomastoideus

longus colli
ventralis cranialis

THIRD LAYER

longus colli
ventralis medialis

longus colli
ventralis caudalis

SECOND LAYER

**NECK-VENTRAL VIEW
PLATE 13**

Plate 14   Trunk and Base of Neck   Lateral View

Superficial Layer
1. M. externus abdominis - (See Plate 25)

2. M. intercostales superficiales, superficial intercostal muscles
   FORM AND RELATIONSHIPS: short; deep to fascia of rectus abdominis
      sacrolumbalis; superficial to intercostales externales.
   ORIGIN: uncinate processes, ventral border by fibers.
   INSERTION: rib, caudal to preceding uncinate process, by fibers.
   ACTION: draws thoracic ribs caudally.

3. M. levatores costarum - (See Plate 24)
4. M. longissimus dorsi - (See Plate 15)
5. M. longus colli dorsalis - (See Plate 8)
6. M. longus colli ventralis caudalis - (See Plate 13)
7. M. longus colli ventralis medialis - (See Plate 13)
8. M. obliqui colli - (See Plate 9)

9. M. sacrolumbalis, cranial and caudal fasciculus
   FORM AND RELATIONSHIPS: composed of two fasciculi; cranial fasciculus
      is long straplike; the caudal is triangular; deep to rhomboideus,
      serratus dorsalis, sartorius and scapula; superficial to levatores
      costarum, scalenius and longissimus dorsi.
   ORIGIN: caudal fasciculus, by fibers from cranial fasciculus in the
      region of the third to fifth thoracic ribs; ilium, cranial border from
      caudal fasciculus by fibers.
   INSERTION: cervical vertebrae, thirteen and fourteen, from cranial
      fasciculus by fibers; thoracic vertebrae three, four, five from caudal
      fasciculus by fascia and fibers.
   ACTION: elevates thorax.

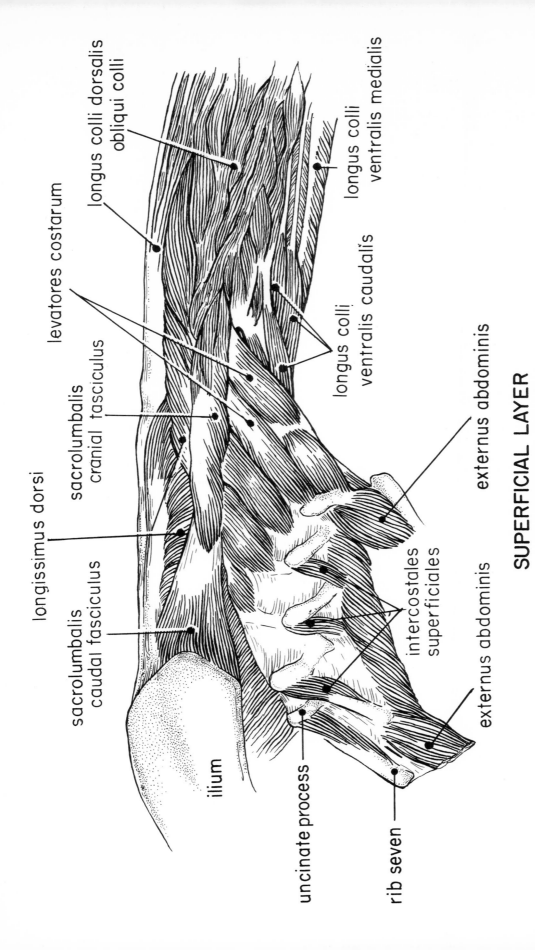

longus colli dorsalis
obliqui colli

longus colli
ventralis medialis

levatores costarum

longus colli
ventralis caudalis

sacrolumbalis
cranial fasciculus

longissimus dorsi

longus colli
ventralis caudalis

externus abdominis

sacrolumbalis
caudal fasciculus

intercostales
superficiales

externus abdominis

ilium

externus abdominis

uncinate process

rib seven

SUPERFICIAL LAYER

TRUNK AND BASE OF NECK–LATERAL VIEW
PLATE 14

Plate 15   Trunk and Base of Neck   Lateral View

Second Layer

1. M. intercostales externales, external intercostal muscle
   FORM AND RELATIONSHIPS: five in number, thin, short and flat; deep to
      pectoralis superficialis, teres, serratus ventralis, intercostales
      superficiales; superficial to pleura by intercostales internales by
      third, fourth and fifth intercostales externales.
   ORIGIN: second through sixth thoracic ribs, caudal border and uncinate
      processes, ventral borders by fibers.
   INSERTION: third through seventh thoracic rib, cranial borders ventral
      to uncinate process by fibers.
   ACTION: draws preceding rib caudally or succeeding rib cranially.

2. M. levatores costarum - (See Plate 24)

3. M. longissimus dorsi, dorsal longissimus
   FORM AND RELATIONSHIPS: composed of a number of inseparable fasciculi;
      the caudal fasciculus, the most distinct is fusiform; the cranial
      fasciculi forms a straplike complex unit; deep to sacrolumbalis,
      rhomboideus; superficial to transverse processes of the sacral, lumbar,
      and thoracic ribs.
   ORIGIN: ilium, medioventral border, synsacral and thoracic vertebrae,
      dorsal spines and transverse processes, by fibers.
   INSERTION: lumbar, thoracic, and cervical vertebrae, transverse pro-
      cesses and spines, by tendons.
   ACTION: elevates thorax and base of neck.

4. M. longus colli dorsalis - (See Plate 8)
5. M. longus colli ventralis caudalis - (See Plate 13)
6. M. longus colli ventralis medialis - (See Plate 13)

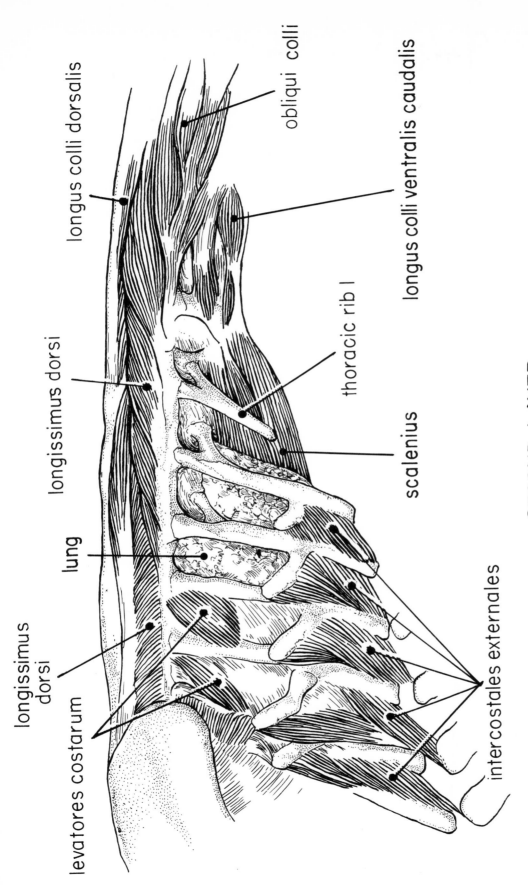

longus colli dorsalis

obliqui colli

longus colli ventralis caudalis

longissimus dorsi

thoracic rib I

scalenius

lung

longissimus
dorsi

levatores costarum

intercostales externales

SECOND LAYER

TRUNK AND BASE OF NECK–LATERAL VIEW
PLATE 15

Plate 16   Trunk and Shoulder   Dorsal View

Superficial
1. M. cutaneus cleidodorsalis - (See Plate 7)

2. M. cutaneus costohumeralis, costohumeral cutaneous muscle
   FORM AND RELATIONSHIPS: long and straplike, superficial and lateral on
      trunk; under the skin, sartorius, triceps and intercostales externales;
      over serratus magnus, teres major and cranial fan of latissimus dorsi.
   ORIGIN: articulation of thoracic rib six with sternal rib four.
   INSERTION: humeral pteryla, by fibers, in common with insertion of
      cutaneus iliacus.
   ACTION: elevates feathers of humeral pteryla.

3. M. cutaneus iliacus, cutaneous muscle of the flank
   FORM AND RELATIONSHIPS: short, thin and straplike; just under the skin;
      over caudal and cranial fans of latissimus dorsi.
   ORIGIN: fascia sling over thoracic vertebra five and ilium, by fibers,
      in common with cutaneus spinalis dorsalis.
   INSERTION: humeral pteryla, by fibers.
   ACTION: elevates feathers of humeral pteryla.

4. M. cutaneus spinalis dorsalis, dorsal cutaneous muscle of the cervico-
   thoracic area
   FORM AND RELATIONSHIPS: long and straplike; most dorsal of the cutaneous
      muscles; just under the skin; over latissimus dorsi and longus colli
      dorsalis.
   ORIGIN: lumbodorsal fascia, by fibers, in common with cutaneus iliacus.
   INSERTION: spinal pteryla at about thirteenth cervical vertebra, by
      fibers, in common with cutaneus cleidodorsalis; fibers spread out
      indistinctly on the skin.
   ACTION: with cutaneus cleidodorsalis elevates feathers of dorsal
      pteryla.

5. M. deltoideus - (See Plate 17)

6. M. latissimus dorsi, wide dorsal muscle
   FORM AND RELATIONSHIPS: two-headed muscle; cranial and caudal heads;
      cranial head is fan-shaped; deep to skin, cutaneus spinalis dorsalis,
      caput dorsale of triceps; superficial to teres major; trapezius and
      caput ventrale and internale of the triceps; caudal head short and
      thick; deep to cutaneus iliacus, skin; superficial to trapezius.
   ORIGIN: cranial head: first, second and third thoracic vertebrae, dor-
      sal spines, by fascia.
            caudal head: fourth and fifth thoracic vertebrae, dorsal
      spines, by fascia, and fascia at the origin of sartorius and dorsal
      distal border of the scapula.
   INSERTION: cranial head: humerus, caudally and one-third distally, by
      fibers.
            caudal head: head of humerus, caudal border by loose fascia.
   ACTION: flexes and abducts brachium.

7. M. sacrolumbalis - (See Plate 14)
8. M. sartorius - (See Plate 32)
9. M. serratus magnus - (See Plate 18)
10. M. teres - (See Plate 17)
11. M. trapezius - (See Plate 18)
12. M. triceps - (See Plates 17 & 18)

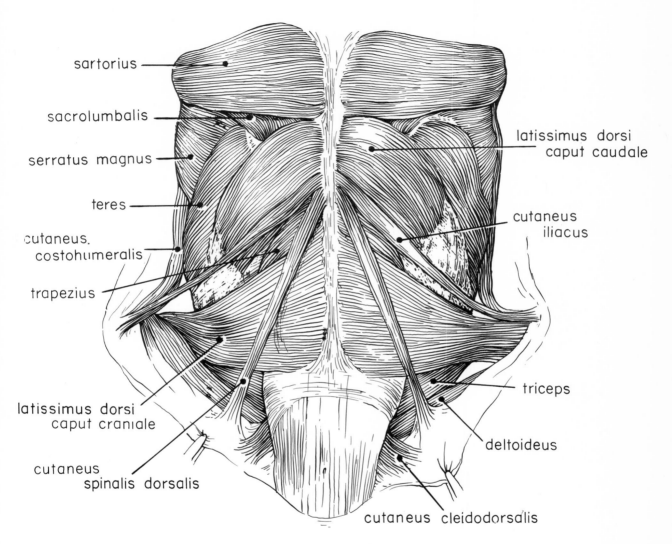

sartorius

sacrolumbalis

serratus magnus

teres

cutaneus. costohumeralis

trapezius

latissimus dorsi caput craniale

cutaneus spinalis dorsalis

latissimus dorsi caput caudale

cutaneus iliacus

triceps

deltoideus

cutaneus cleidodorsalis

SUPERFICIAL LAYER

TRUNK AND SHOULDER-DORSAL VIEW
PLATE 16

Plate 17   Trunk and Shoulder   Dorsal View

Second Layer
  1. M. biceps brachii - (See Plate 54)
  2. M. cutaneus costohumeralis - (See Plate 16)

  3. M. deltoideus, the deltoid
      FORM AND RELATIONSHIPS: long, thick and tapered; just under skin; over
        scapulohumeralis maximus, caput internale of triceps and insertion of
        latissimus dorsi; caudal to proximal portion of patagialis; cranial to
        caput dorsale of triceps.
      ORIGIN: scapula, from proximodorsal aspect just caudal to origin of
        scapulohumeralis maximus by fibers.
      INSERTION: humerus, distocaudal two-thirds by a tendon; inserting
        tendon continues distally to join the inserting tendon of triceps.
      ACTION: flexes and abducts brachium.

  4. M. interspinales craniales - (See Plate 8)
  5. M. latissimus dorsi, caput caudale - (See Plate 16)
  6. M. longissimus dorsi, cranial fan - (See Plate 15)
  7. M. longus colli dorsalis - (See Plate 8)
  8. M. longus colli ventrales - (See Plate 13)
  9. M. patagialis - (See Plate 20)
 10. M. sacrolumbalis - (See Plate 14)
 11. M. sartorius - (See Plate 32)
 12. M. serratus magnus - (See Plate 18)

 13. M. teres
      FORM AND RELATIONSHIPS: largest muscle of scapular region; deep to
        latissimus dorsi, tensor patagii caudalis; superficial to serratus
        magnus, serratus ventralis, intercostales externales and scapula.
      ORIGIN: scapula, lateral and ventral borders by fibers.
      INSERTION: humeral crest, by a tendon and to tendon of tensor patagii
        caudalis by a small slip of fibers.
      ACTION: pronates and flexes brachium.

 14. M. trapezius - (See Plate 18)

 15. M. triceps, the triceps, a three-headed muscle (caputi dorsale, ventrale
      and internale) along the medial border of the humerus.
      a. caput dorsale
          FORM AND RELATIONSHIPS: long, fusiform; just under the skin;
            medial to biceps brachii and deltoideus; dorsal to caputi,
            internale and ventrale and to insertion of latissimus dorsi.
          ORIGIN: scapula, proximodorsally, by a tendon.
          INSERTION: ulna, olecranon process by tendon.
          ACTION: extends antibrachium.
      b. caput internale - (See Plate 18)
      c. caput ventrale
          FORM AND RELATIONSHIPS: triangular because of three originating
            fasciculi; under skin and tensor patagi caudalis; ventral to
            latissimus dorsi and caput internale; along ventral border of
            humerus.
          ORIGIN: (a) humerus, near head, (b) humerus, pneumatic fossa,
            (c) humerus, bicipital crest and ventrocaudal border.
          INSERTION: ulna, olecranon process by tendon.
          ACTION: extends antibrachium.

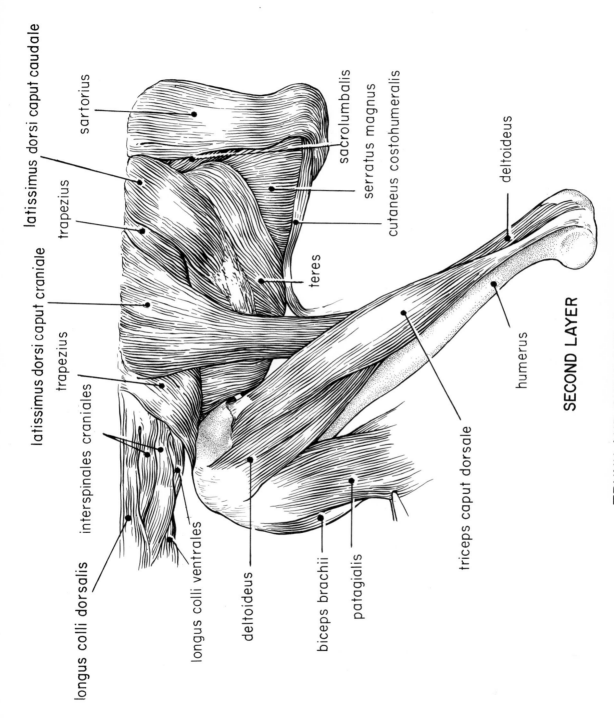

latissimus dorsi caput caudale

sartorius

sacrolumbalis

serratus magnus

cutaneus costohumeralis

deltoideus

latissimus dorsi caput craniale

trapezius

trapezius

teres

humerus

interspinales craniales

longus colli dorsalis

longus colli ventrales

deltoideus

biceps brachii

patagialis

triceps caput dorsale

SECOND LAYER

TRUNK AND SHOULDER-DORSAL VIEW
PLATE 17

Plate 18   Trunk and Shoulder   Dorsal View

Third Layer
1. M. coracobrachialis dorsalis tendon - (See Plate 19)
2. M. latissimus dorsi, cranial fan - (See Plate 16)
3. M. pectoralis profundus tendon - (See Plate 21)
4. M. pectoralis superficialis - (See Plate 20)

5. M. rhomboideus, rhomboid muscle
     FORM AND RELATIONSHIPS: thin and flat; deep to trapezius latissimus
        dorsi; superficial to longissimus dorsi.
     ORIGIN: thoracic vertebrae one through five, dorsal spines, by fibers
        and fascia.
     INSERTION: scapula, caudal two-thirds on dorsomedial surface, by fibers.
     ACTION: elevates caudal part of scapula.

6. M. sacrolumbalis - (See Plate 14)
7. M. sartorius - (See Plate 32)

8. M. scapulohumeralis maximus, the large scapulohumeral muscle
     FORM AND RELATIONSHIPS: broad, flat, tapering; under patagialis and
        deltoideus; caudal to pectoralis superficialis over the shoulder
        (omobrachium) articulations, originating tendon of biceps brachii and
        inserting tendon of pectoralis profundus.
     ORIGIN: coracoid, dorsomedial tuberosity, by fibers; scapula,
        proximodorsal portion, by fibers.
     INSERTION: humerus, proximodorsal tuberosity deltoid crest, by fibers.
     ACTION: abducts brachium.

9. M. serratus magnus
     FORM AND RELATIONSHIPS: triangular, flat and thin; deep to skin,
        sartorius, teres major; superficial to intercostales externales of
        the fourth through sixth ribs and uncinate processes of third through
        fifth ribs.
     ORIGIN: vertebral ribs, four through six ventral to articulation of
        the uncinates processes, by fascia.
     INSERTION: scapula, ventrocaudal angle, by fibers.
     ACTION: depresses caudal part of scapula.

10. M. tensor patagii longus - (See Plate 20)
11. M. teres - (See Plate 17)

12. M. trapezius
     FORM AND RELATIONSHIPS: thin and flat; deep to latissimus dorsi;
        superficial to rhomboideus.
     ORIGIN: thoracic vertebrae four and five, dorsal border of fused
        spines, by fibers and thoracic vertebrae one through four, by fascia.
     INSERTION: scapula, vertebral border and dorsomedial surface from the
        dorsal angle to the neck, by fibers.
     ACTION: elevates scapula, thereby, elevating cranial portion of sternum.

13. M. triceps - (See Also Plate 17)
     caput internale
        FORM AND RELATIONSHIPS: long and thin; along caudal surface of
           humerus; under caputi dorsale and ventrale triceps; dorsal to
           inserting fibers of latissimus dorsi.
        ORIGIN: humerus, along entire caudal border, by fibers.
        INSERTION: ulna, olecranon process, by fibers.
        ACTION: extends antibrachium.

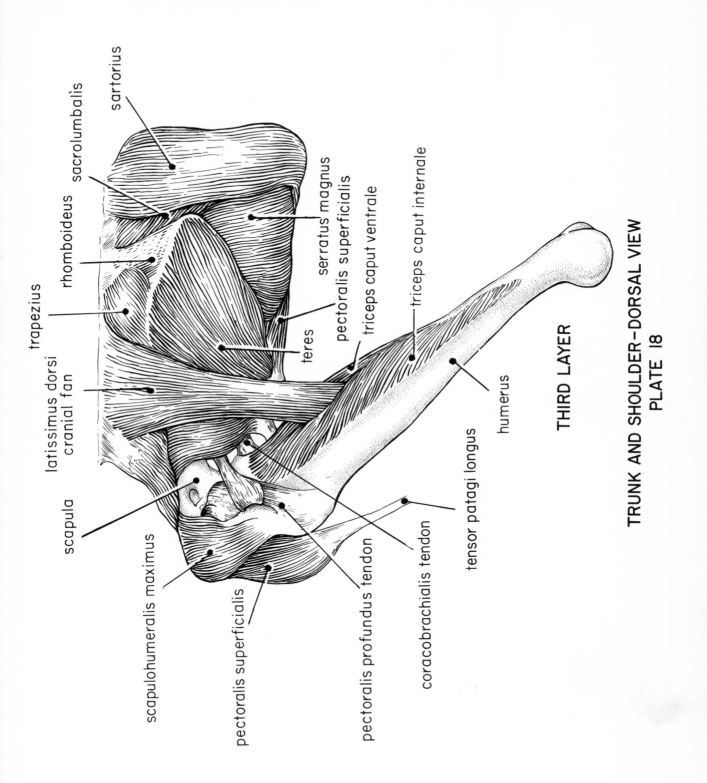

trapezius

sartorius

sacrolumbalis

rhomboideus

serratus magnus

pectoralis superficialis

triceps caput ventrale

triceps caput internale

latissimus dorsi
cranial fan

teres

scapula

humerus

scapulohumeralis maximus

pectoralis superficialis

pectoralis profundus tendon

coracobrachialis tendon

tensor patagi longus

THIRD LAYER

TRUNK AND SHOULDER—DORSAL VIEW
PLATE 18

Fourth Layer

1. M. coracobrachialis dorsalis, dorsal coracobrachial muscle
   FORM AND RELATIONSHIPS: fusiform; lying between furcula and coracoid;
   under pectoralis superficialis; over the pleural cavity.
   ORIGIN: manubrium, laterally by fibers; coracoid, dorsoproximal
   two-thirds, by fibers.
   INSERTION: humerus deltoid crest, by a tendon.
   ACTION: extends brachium.

2. M. coracobrachialis ventralis, ventral coracobrachial muscle
   FORM AND RELATIONSHIPS: long and triangular; two fasciculi; under
   pectoralis superficialis, dorsolateral to pectoralis profundus;
   over coracoid, sternocoracoideus and subcoracoideus.
   ORIGIN: coracoid, dorsal border, by fibers; sternum, ventrolateral part
   of craniolateral process, by fibers.
   INSERTION: humerus, pneumatic fossa, by a tendon.
   ACTION: adducts brachium.

3. M. coracohumeralis, coracohumeral muscle
   FORM AND RELATIONSHIPS: fusiform; under pectoralis superficialis and
   inserting tendon of biceps brachii.
   ORIGIN: coracoid, proximomedial tuberosity, by heavy tendon.
   INSERTION: humerus, base of deltoid crest ventrally, by fibers.
   ACTION: extends brachium.

4. M. intercostale externale - (See Plate 15)
5. M. levatores costarum - (See Plate 24)
6. M. pectoralis profundus tendon - (See Plate 21)
7. M. rhomboideus - (See Plate 18)
8. M. sacrolumbalis - (See Plate 14)
9. M. sartorius - (See Plate 32)

10. M. scapulohumeralis minimus, small scapulohumeral muscle
    FORM AND RELATIONSHIPS: small, cordlike; under caput ventrale and caput
    internale of triceps; over inserting tendon of coracobrachialis
    ventralis.
    ORIGIN: scapular neck, ventral and just cranial to scapulohumeralis
    ligament, by fibers.
    INSERTION: humerus, pneumatic fossa just proximal to pneumatic foramen,
    by fibers.
    ACTION: pronates brachium.

11. M. serratus dorsalis, dorsal serrate muscle
    FORM AND RELATIONSHIPS: composed of three short and flat fasciculi;
    deep to scapula; superficial to levatores costarum, sacrolumbalis.
    ORIGIN: first rib, cranial border by fibers from cranial fasciculus;
    second rib, caudal border by fibers from the medial and caudal
    fasciculi.
    INSERTION: scapula, medial surface cranial to its dorsal and ventral
    angles by fibers from the three fasciculi.
    ACTION: elevates thoracic ribs dorsocaudally.

12. M. serratus magnus - (See Plate 18)

13. M. serratus ventralis, ventral serrate muscle
    FORM AND RELATIONSHIPS: small; deep to teres, pectoralis superficialis;

and superficial to <u>levatores</u> <u>costarum</u> of the second rib.

ORIGIN: second rib, lateral border ventral to articulation of the uncinate process, by fibers.

INSERTION: scapula, ventral border three cm. distal to glenoid facet by fascia.

ACTION: elevates asternal rib II.

14. <u>M</u>. <u>subcoracoideus</u> - (See Plate 23)

15. <u>M</u>. <u>subscapularis</u>, the subscapular muscle

FORM AND RELATIONSHIPS: two triangular fasciculi; just under scapula anteriorly; over peritoneum and first <u>levator</u> <u>costarum</u>.

ORIGIN: scapula, by fibers, from craniomedial fourth and the coracoid, proximomedial surface, by fibers.

INSERTION: on tendon of <u>subcoracoideus</u>.

ACTION: with the <u>subcoracoideus</u> it pronates and flexes brachium.

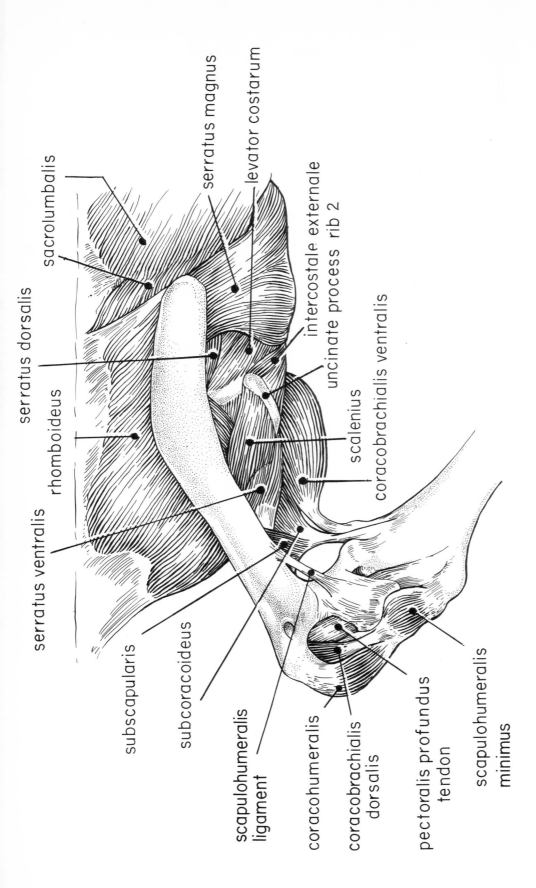

sacrolumbalis

serratus magnus

levator costarum

serratus dorsalis

intercostale externale

uncinate process rib 2

rhomboideus

scalenius

coracobrachialis ventralis

serratus ventralis

subscapularis

subcoracoideus

scapulohumeralis ligament

coracohumeralis

coracobrachialis dorsalis

pectoralis profundus tendon

scapulohumeralis minimus

FOURTH LAYER

TRUNK AND SHOULDER–DORSAL VIEW
PLATE 19

Plate 20   Trunk and Torso   Lateral View

Superficial Layer

1. M. basirectricales, the basirectrical muscle
    FORM AND RELATIONSHIPS: fibers of this muscle are folded over shafts of
        caudal rectrices; deep to skin, levator rectricum, depressor
        rectricum and caudalis lateralis; superficial to shafts of caudal
        rectrices.
    ORIGIN: pygostyle, lateral surface, by fibers.
    INSERTION: caudal rectrices, shafts, by fascia.
    ACTION: spreads caudal rectrices laterally.

2. M. caudalis lateralis - (See Plate 30)
3. M. cutaneus costohumeralis - (See Plate 16)

4. M. cutaneus pectoralis caudalis, caudal cutaneous muscle of the breast
    FORM AND RELATIONSHIPS: thin; straplike; just under the skin; over
        pectoralis superficialis.
    ORIGIN: sternum, fascia over caudal lateral process, by fibers.
    INSERTION: lateral and ventral pteryla, by fibers, in common with
        cutaneus pectoralis cranialis.
    ACTION: elevates feathers of lateral and ventral pteryla.

5. M. cutaneus pectoralis cranialis, the cranial cutaneus muscle of the
    breast
    FORM AND RELATIONSHIPS: broad, flat and triangular; over pectoralis
        superficialis; just under the skin.
    ORIGIN: inserting fascia of teres, by fibers, as three united straplike
        fasciculi.
    INSERTION: lateral and ventral pteryla, by fibers; the most cranial
        fasciculus sends slips to tendon of tensor patagii caudalis.
    ACTION: elevation of feathers of lateral and ventral pteryla.

6. M. depressor caudae - (See Plate 22)
7. M. depressor rectricum - (See Plate 22)
8. M. eversor urodeum - (See Plate 30)
9. M. externus abdominis - (See Plate 25)
10. M. levator caudae - (See Plate 27)
11. M. levator rectricum - (See Plate 27)

12. M. patagialis, patagial muscle
    FORM AND RELATIONSHIPS: wide, straplike; just under skin; caudal to
        pectoralis superficialis; cranial to deltoideus; over and also cranial
        to scapulohumeralis maximus.
    ORIGIN: terminal fascia of pectoralis superficialis, over the dorso-
        distal portion of coracoid, by fibers.
    INSERTION: skin of wing, by extensive fascia; to fascia in proximal
        region of extensor carpi radialis superficialis.
    ACTION: tenses the wing fold.

13. M. pectoralis superficialis, superficial pectoral muscle
    FORM AND RELATIONSHIPS: the largest muscle of the turkey; broad, flat
        and fusiform; just under skin; three fasciculi.
    ORIGIN: (a) furcula, lateral border, by fibers.
            (b) keel, ventral crest, by fascia.
            (c) sternal ribs, by fibers, from fascia covering sternal
                ribs and sternal processes.

INSERTION: humerus, laterodistal part of deltoid crest, by broad
   tendinous fascia; _teres_, by thin fascia.
ACTION: adducts brachium and omobrachium ventromedially.

14. M. _tensor patagii caudalis_, the caudal tensor of the skin of wing
   FORM AND RELATIONSHIPS: mostly tendinous on caudal aspect of brachium;
      just under skin; over _teres_, _caput ventrale_ of _triceps_ and the
      pectoralis superficialis; receives some fibers from _cutaneus
      pectoralis cranialis_.
   ORIGIN: _subcoracoideus_, and fascia of axial air sac, by tendon.
      (This origin receives a small inserting slip from the _teres_.)
   INSERTION: skin of antibrachium by fascia.
   ACTION: tenses caudal skin of antibrachium and spreads the secondary
      feathers.

15. M. _tensor patagii longus_, the long tensor of the wing fold
   FORM AND RELATIONSHIPS: not muscular in the turkey; long, tendinous
      forming the base of a triangle between brachium and antibrachium when
      wing is extended; just under the skin.
   ORIGIN: pectoralis superficialis; a slip from _patagialis_.
   INSERTION: sesamoid at distal extremity of radius.
   ACTION: tenses patagium between shoulder and distal end of radius.

16. M. _transversus perinei_ - (See Plate 30)
17. M. _triceps caput internale_ - (See Plate 18)
18. M. _triceps caput ventrale_ - (See Plate 17)

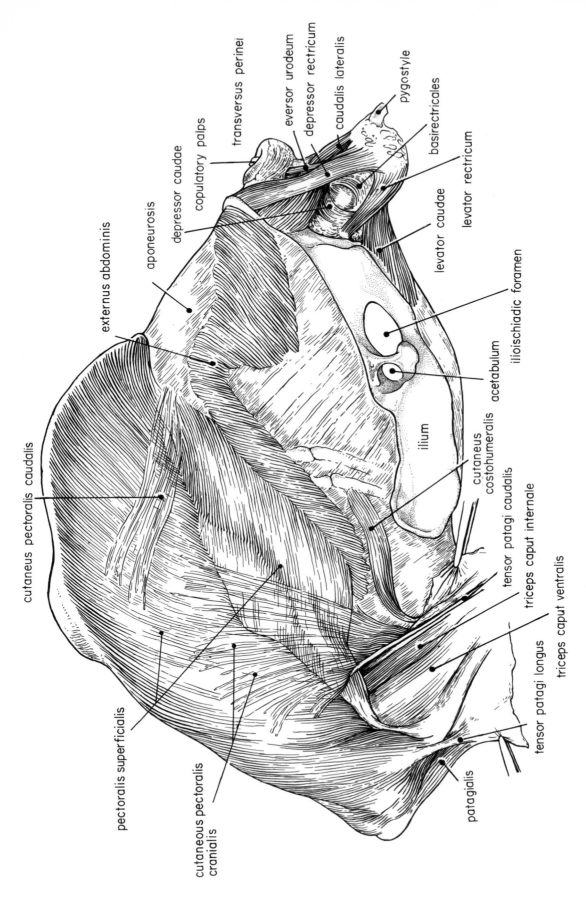

cutaneus pectoralis caudalis

externus abdominis

aponeurosis

depressor caudae

copulatory palps

transversus perinei

eversor urodeum

depressor rectricum

caudalis lateralis

pygostyle

basirectricales

levator rectricum

levator caudae

ilioischiadic foramen

acetabulum

cutaneus costohumeralis

ilium

tensor patagi caudalis

triceps caput ventralis

tensor patagi internale

tensor patagi longus

triceps caput ventralis

patagialis

cutaneous pectoralis cranialis

pectoralis superficialis

TRUNK AND TORSO–LEFT–LATERAL VIEW
PLATE 20

Plate 21   Trunk and Torso   Left Lateral View

Second Layer
1. M. basirectricales - (See Plate 20)
2. M. coracobrachiales ventralis - (See Plate 19)
3. M. depressor caudae - (See Plate 22)
4. M. eversor urodeum - (See Plate 30)
5. M. externus abdominis - (See Plate 25)
6. M. intercostales externales - (See Plate 15)
7. M. levator caudae - (See Plate 27)
8. M. levator rectricum - (See Plate 27)

9. M. obliquus internus abdominis, the internal oblique muscle of the
   abdomen
     FORM AND RELATIONSHIPS: triangular, flat; deep to fascia of externus
       abdominis; superficial to transversus abdominis.
     ORIGIN: pubis, ventral border cranial-third; and ilium, cranioventral
       border, by fascia.
     INSERTION: sternal rib five, caudal border; thoracic rib seven, caudal
       border, by fascia.
     ACTION: compresses dorsal abdomen and draws ribs five, six and seven
       caudally.

10. M. patagialis - (See Plate 20)

11. M. pectoralis profundus, deep pectoral muscle
      FORM AND RELATIONSHIPS: a large breast muscle, long and fusiform; two
        fasciculi; mostly surrounded by pectoralis superficialis; lies over
        keel, sternum, coracoid and furcula; ventral to coracobrachialis
        ventralis.
      ORIGIN: keel, lateral surface, by fibers; sternum, cranial carinal
        margin, by fibers; furcula, lateral distal aspect, by fascia.
      INSERTION: humerus, area just distal to lateral aspect of deltoid
        crest, by a tendon.
      ACTION: abducts brachium.

12. M. pectoralis superficialis - (See Plate 20)

13. M. rectus abdominis, the rectus of the abdomen
      FORM AND RELATIONSHIPS: flat, thin, parallelogram; deep to externus
        abdominis; superficial to transversus abdominis.
      ORIGIN: sternum, dorsolateral process caudal angle, by fibers; caudo-
        lateral process, medial border, by fascia and fibers.
      INSERTION: pubis, ventral border caudal third, by fascia; caudal
        median raphe, by fascia.
      ACTION: compresses abdomen.

14. M. scalenius - (See Plate 25)
15. M. serratus magnus - (See Plate 18)

16. M. sphincter ani, anal sphincter
      FORM AND RELATIONSHIPS: sphincter; deep to skin; superficial to
        transversus perinei.
      ORIGIN AND INSERTION: from and to itself, by fibers.
      ACTION: constricts anal opening.

17. M. sternocostales - (See Plate 23)
18. M. subscapularis - (See Plate 19)
19. M. tensor patagii caudalis - (See Plate 20)

20. <u>M</u>. <u>teres</u> - (See Plate 17)
21. <u>M</u>. <u>transversus</u> <u>perinei</u> - (See Plate 30)
22. <u>M</u>. <u>triceps</u> <u>caput</u> <u>internale</u> - (See Plate 18)
23. <u>M</u>. <u>triceps</u> <u>caput</u> <u>ventrale</u> - (See Plate 17)

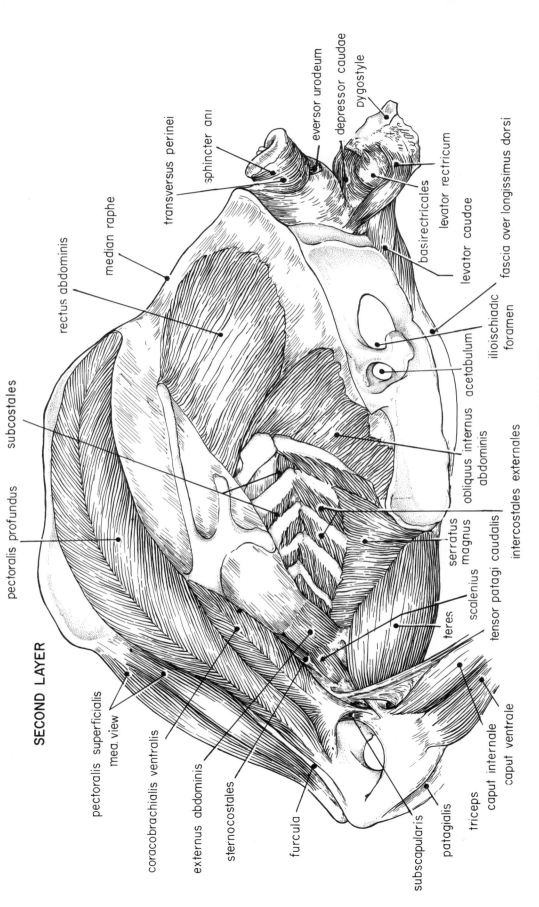

SECOND LAYER

eversor urodeum

transversus perinei

sphincter ani

depressor caudae

pygostyle

median raphe

rectus abdominis

basirectricales

levator rectricum

levator caudae

fascia over longissimus dorsi

subcostales

ilioischiadic foramen

acetabulum

obliquus internus abdominis

intercostales externales

pectoralis profundus

serratus magnus

teres

scalenius

tensor patagi caudalis

pectoralis superficialis
med. view

coracobrachialis ventralis

externus abdominis

sternocostales

furcula

subscapularis

patagialis

triceps

caput internale

caput ventrale

TRUNK AND TORSO – LEFT LATERAL VIEW
PLATE 21

Plate 22   Trunk and Torso   Left Lateral View

Third Layer
1. M. caudalis lateralis - (See Plate 30)
2. M. coracobrachialis dorsalis - (See Plate 19)

3. M. depressor caudae, depressor of the tail
      FORM AND RELATIONSHIPS: triangular, thick and short; deep to caudalis
         lateralis, levator rectricum; superficial to caudal vertebrae, ventral
         surfaces of transverse processes and centra.
      ORIGIN: caudal vertebrae one, transverse process ventral surface, by
         fibers.
      INSERTION: pygostyle, transverse process ventral surface, by fibers.
      ACTION: depresses caudal vertebrae.

4. M. depressor rectricum, depressor of retrices
      FORM AND RELATIONSHIPS: straplike, flat and narrow; deep to the skin;
         superficial to eversor urodeum, caudalis lateralis, lateralis
         rectricum.
      ORIGIN: pubis, ventral and caudal border, by fibers.
      INSERTION: fascia of rectrices one to five, in common with levator
         rectricum.
      ACTION: depresses caudal rectrix.

5. M. intercostales internales, internal intercostals
      FORM AND RELATIONSHIPS: three in number, small; deep to intercostales
         externales, superficial to abdominal peritoneum.
      ORIGIN: vertebral ribs four, five and six, caudal borders ventral to
         uncinate process, by fibers.
      INSERTION: vertebral ribs five, six and seven, cranial border ventral
         to the uncinate process, by fibers.
      ACTION: draws ribs cranially.

6. M. intercostales superficialis - (See Plate 14)
7. M. levator caudae - (See Plate 27)
8. M. levatores costarum - (See Plate 24)
9. M. sacrolumbalis - (See Plate 14)
10. M. scalenius - (See Plate 25)
11. M. serratus dorsalis - (See Plate 19)

12. M. sternocoracoideus, sternocoracoid muscle
      FORM AND RELATIONSHIPS: broad, flat and short; under coracobrachialis
         ventralis; over subcoracoideus and pleural peritoneum.
      ORIGIN: sternum, laterocranial process, ventral border, by fibers.
      INSERTION: coracoid, dorsomedial border, by fibers.
      ACTION: draws coracoid caudally.

13. M. sternocostales - (See Plate 24)
14. M. subscapularis - (See Plate 19)

15. M. transversus abdominis, the transverse muscle of the abdomen
      FORM AND RELATIONSHIPS: flat, thin; deep to obliquus internus abdominis,
         rectus abdominis, sternal ribs four & five and thoracic ribs five, six
         and seven; superficial to abdominal peritoneum.
      ORIGIN: pubis, ventral border by fibers; ilium, cranioventral border by
         fascia.
      INSERTION: caudal median raphe and sternum, laterocaudal process by
         fascia.
      ACTION: compresses abdomen.

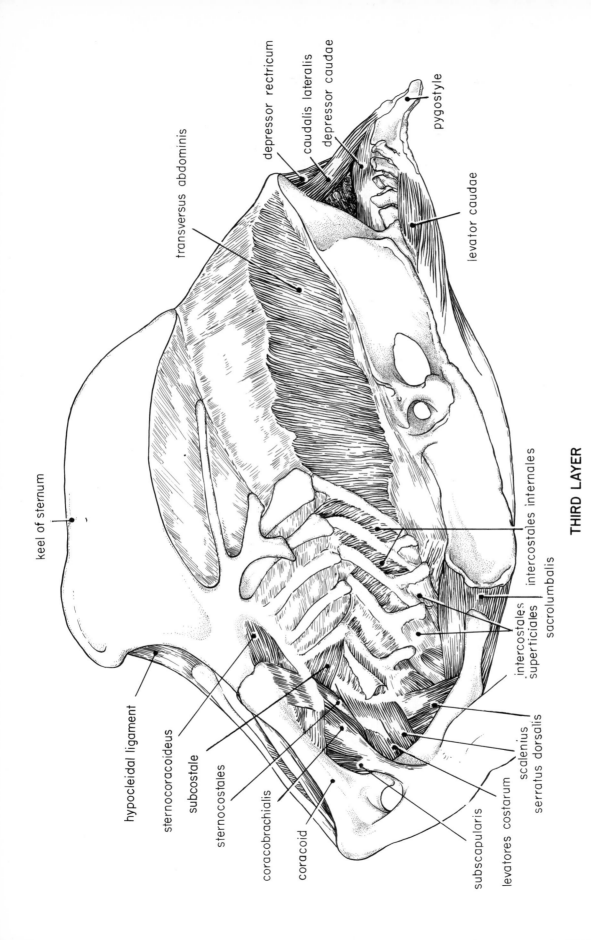

keel of sternum

transversus abdominis

depressor rectricum

caudalis lateralis

depressor caudae

pygostyle

levator caudae

intercostales internales

sacrolumbalis

intercostales
superficiales

serratus dorsalis

scalenius

levatores costarum

subscapularis

coracoid

coracobrachialis

sternocostales

subcostale

sternocoracoideus

hypocleidal ligament

THIRD LAYER

TRUNK AND TORSO–LEFT LATERAL VIEW
PLATE 22

Plate 23   Trunk and Torso   Internal Medial View

First Layer
1. M. caudalis lateralis - (See Plate 30)
2. M. coracobrachialis dorsalis - (See Plate 19)
3. M. depressor caudae - (See Plate 22)

4. M. diaphragma, the diaphragm
    FORM AND RELATIONSHIPS: composed of three groups of fasciculi; cranial,
      medial and caudal.
    ORIGIN: sternal rib two and four, medial surface by fibers from the
      cranial fasciculus; thoracic rib six; articulation of thoracic rib six
      and sternal rib four, medial surfaces by three separate fasciculi of
      the medial fasciculus by fibers; transversus abdominis, by fascia; and
      thoracic rib seven, medial surface by the caudal fasciculi.
    INSERTION: pleural membrane surrounding lungs, separately by each
      fasciculus.
    ACTION: expansion of pleura surrounding lungs.

5. M. gluteus medius - (See Plate 29)
6. M. longus colli ventrales - (See Plate 13)

7. M. obturator internus, the internal obturator
    FORM AND RELATIONSHIPS: two heads with a common insertion; lateral
      head (caput laterale) is superficial to ilium, ischium, ilioischiadic
      foramen, medial head (caput mediale) lies on medial surface of ischium.
    ORIGIN: lateral head - ilium, ischium, ilioischiadic fossa; medial
      head - ischium, medial surface.
    INSERTION: femur, greater trochanter caudomedial face, by a tendon.
    ACTION: adducts thigh and draws it caudally.

8. M. pectoralis superficialis - (See Plate 20)
9. M. semitendinosus - (See Plate 33)
10. M. sternocoracoideus - (See Plate 22)

11. M. sternocostales
    FORM AND RELATIONSHIPS: two in number, short; deep to pectoralis
      superficialis, externus abdominis; superficial to thoracic pleura.
    ORIGIN: sternum, craniolateral process, lateral aspect of the apex by
      first (cranial) sternocostale and medial aspect of the apex by a tendon
      from the second (caudal) sternocostale.
    INSERTION: thoracic rib one, apex by fibers and tendon of the first
      sternocostale; and thoracic rib two, apex medial aspect by fibers of
      the second sternocostale.
    ACTION: depresses asternal ribs one and two.

12. M. sternotrachealis, sternotracheal muscle
    FORM AND RELATIONSHIPS: long and cylindrical; under esophagus cranially;
      over the crop; lateral to trachea and pleural peritoneum.
    ORIGIN: sternum, craniolateral process, by fibers.
    INSERTION: trachea, laterally by four fasciculi; about one-fourth the
      distance cranial to bronchi.
    ACTION: pulls trachea caudally.

13. M. subcoracoideus, subcoracoid muscle
    FORM AND RELATIONSHIPS: thick, triangular; under sternocoracoideus and
      coracoid; over pleural cavity.

ORIGIN: manubrium, by fibers dorsolaterally; coracoid, dorsomedially
   from proximal third, by fibers.
INSERTION: humerus, distal lip of ligamental grooves, by tendon. (This
   tendon also receives fibers of the subscapularis.)
ACTION: pronates and flexes brachium.

14. M. subcostales - (See Plate 24)
15. M. subscapularis - (See Plate 19)
16. M. transversus abdominis - (See Plate 22)

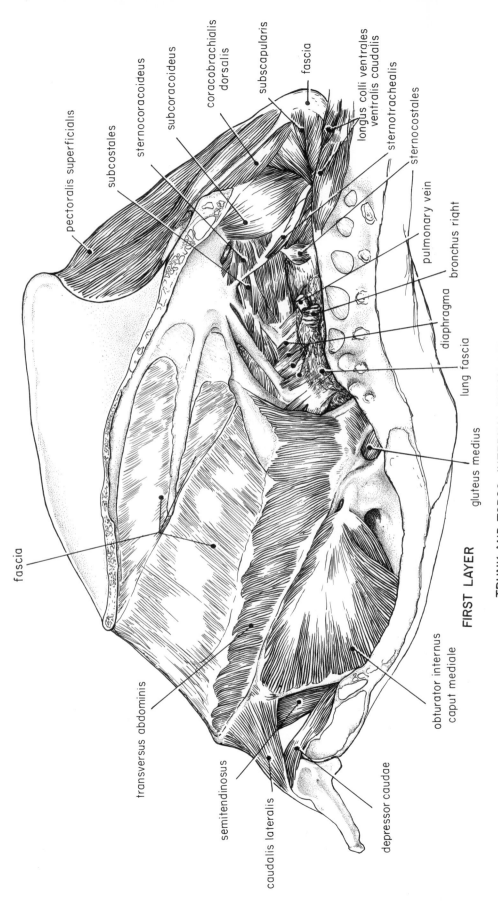

pectoralis superficialis

subcostales

sternocoracoideus

subcoracoideus

coracobrachialis
dorsalis

subscapularis

fascia

longus colli ventrales
ventralis caudalis

sternotrachealis

sternocostales

pulmonary vein

bronchus right

diaphragma

lung fascia

gluteus medius

fascia

transversus abdominis

semitendinosus

caudalis lateralis

obturator internus
caput mediale

depressor caudae

FIRST LAYER

TRUNK AND TORSO—INTERNAL MEDIAL VIEW
PLATE 23

Plate 24   Trunk and Torso   Internal Medial View

Second Layer
1. M. caudalis lateralis - (See Plate 30)
2. M. coracobrachialis dorsalis - (See Plate 19)
3. M. coracobrachialis ventralis - (See Plate 19)
4. M. depressor caudae - (See Plate 22)
5. M. gluteus medius - (See Plate 29)
6. M. intercostales internales - (See Plate 22)

7. M. levatores costarum
   FORM AND RELATIONSHIPS: five flat bands; deep to sacrolumbalis, serratus dorsalis, serratus ventralis, teres; superficial to the pleura.
   ORIGIN: thoracic vertebrae II to V, transverse processes by fascia and fibers.
   INSERTION: thoracic ribs II to VI, cranial borders by fascia and fibers.
   ACTION: draws ribs cranially.

8. M. obliquus internus abdominis - (See Plate 21)
9. M. obturator internus tendon - (See Plate 23)
10. M. rectus abdominis - (See Plate 21)
11. M. scalenius - (See Plate 25)
12. M. scapulohumeralis minimus - (See Plate 19)
13. M. semitendinosus - (See Plate 33)

14. M. serratus dorsalis, dorsal serrate muscle
    FORM AND RELATIONSHIPS: composed of three short and flat fasciculi; deep to scapula; superficial to levatores costarum, and sacrolumbalis.
    ORIGIN: thoracic rib I, cranial border by fibers from cranial fasciculus; thoracic rib II, caudal border by fibers from the medial and caudal fasciculi.
    INSERTION: scapula, medial surface, cranial to its dorsal and ventral angles by fibers from the three fasciculi.
    ACTION: elevates ribs I and II dorsocaudally.

15. M. sternocoracoideus - (See Plate 22)
16. M. sternocostales - (See Plate 23)

17. M. subcostales
    FORM AND RELATIONSHIPS: three in number; the first (cranial) is triangular; the second and third parallelogram; deep to pectoralis superficialis, dorsolateral sternal process; superficial to abdominal peritoneum.
    ORIGIN: sternum, craniolateral process on the caudal border by the first subcostales; sternal rib, caudal border by second subcostales; and sternal rib II by the third subcostales.
    INSERTION: sternal ribs I to III, cranial borders by first, second and third subcostales, respectively.
    ACTION: draws sternal ribs cranially.

18. M. teres - (See Plate 17)

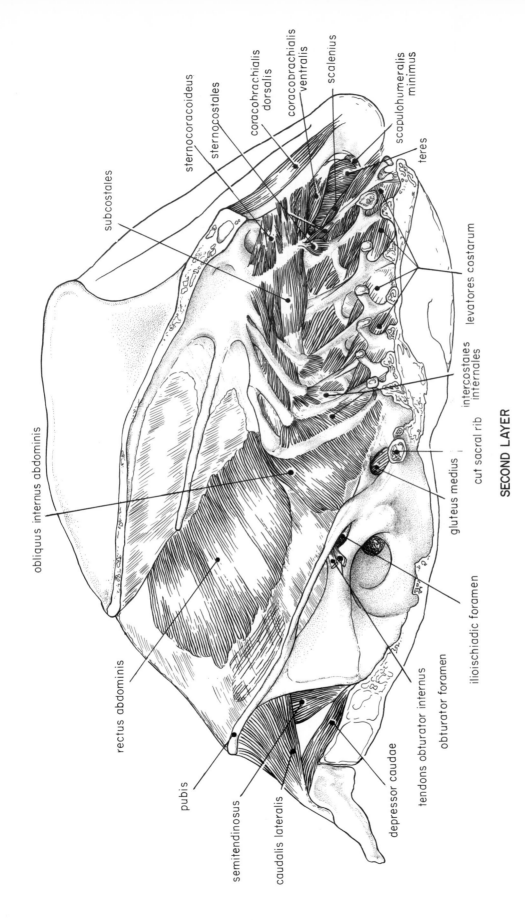

subcostales

sternocoracoideus

sternocostales

coracobrachialis dorsalis

coracobrachialis ventralis

scalenius

scapulohumeralis minimus

teres

levatores costarum

intercostales internales

cut sacral rib

gluteus medius

obliquus internus abdominis

rectus abdominis

pubis

semitendinosus

caudalis lateralis

depressor caudae

tendons obturator internus

obturator foramen

ilioischiadic foramen

SECOND LAYER

TRUNK AND TORSO–INTERNAL MEDIAL VIEW
PLATE 24

Plate 25   Trunk and Torso   Internal Medial View

Third Layer
1. M. caudalis lateralis - (See Plate 30)
2. M. coracobrachialis dorsalis - (See Plate 19)
3. M. coracobrachialis ventralis - (See Plate 19)
4. M. cutaneous cleidodorsalis - (See Plate 7)
5. M. deltoideus - (See Plate 17)
6. M. depressor caudae - (See Plate 22)

7. M. externus abdominis, external muscle of the abdomen
   FORM AND RELATIONSHIPS: long S-shaped; deep to skin, pectoralis
      superficialis and medial muscle of the thigh; superficial to rectus
      abdominis, obliquus internus abdominis, intercostales externales and
      sternal ribs.
   ORIGIN: ischium and pubis, ventral borders; thoracic ribs I to V
      uncinate processes; thoracic ribs I to IV lateral surface.
   INSERTION: median raphe, by fascia; sternum, cranial border of the
      dorsolateral process, by fascia; and dorsal border of sternal rib
      facets, by fascia.
   ACTION: compresses abdomen and ribs.

8. M. intercostales externales - (See Plate 15)
9. M. intercostales superficiales - (See Plate 14)
10. M. pectoralis profundus - (See Plate 21)
11. M. pectoralis superficialis - (See Plate 20)
12. M. sacrolumbalis - (See Plate 14)

13. M. scalenius, the scalenius
    FORM AND RELATIONSHIPS: composed of two fasciculi--cranial and caudal;
       deep to sacrolumbalis, teres, and scapula; superficial to lateral
       surface of thoracic ribs I and II.
    ORIGIN: fourteenth cervical and first thoracic vertebrae, transverse
       processes, dorsal surface.
    INSERTION: thoracic rib I, lateral surface, by fibers from cranial
       fasciculus; thoracic rib I, distocaudal surface, and uncinate process
       of thoracic rib II by fibers.
    ACTION: elevates and draws thoracic ribs I and II cranially.

14. M. semitendinosus - (See Plate 33)
15. M. teres - (See Plate 17)
16. M. trapezius - (See Plate 18)

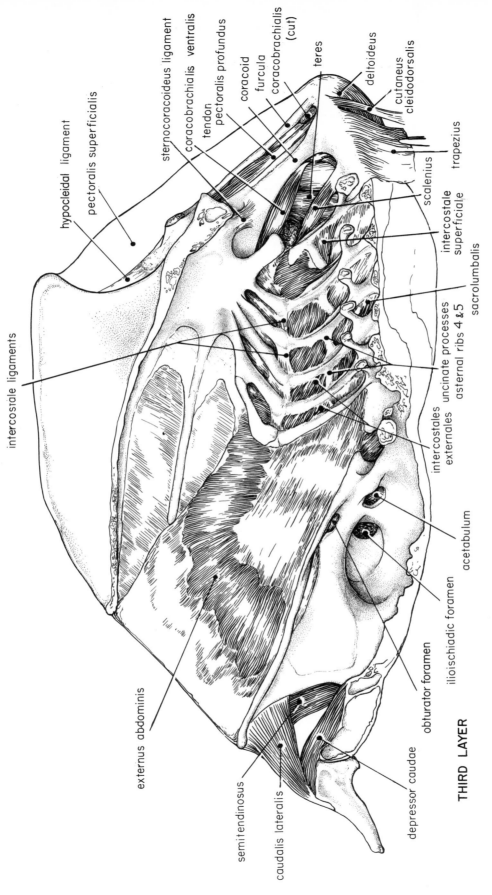

intercostale ligaments

hypocleidal ligament

pectoralis superficialis

sternocoracoideus ligament

coracobrachialis ventralis

tendon

pectoralis profundus

coracoid

furcula

coracobrachialis (cut)

teres

deltoideus

cutaneus cleidodorsalis

trapezius

scalenius

intercostale superficiale

sacrolumbalis

uncinate processes

asternal ribs 4 & 5

intercostales externales

externus abdominis

acetabulum

obturator foramen

ilioischiadic foramen

depressor caudae

caudalis lateralis

semitendinosus

THIRD LAYER

TRUNK AND TORSO – INTERNAL MEDIAL VIEW
PLATE 25

Plate 26   Trunk and Torso   Medial Internal View

Fourth Layer

1. M. adductor magnus - (See Plate 34)
2. M. ambiens - (See Plate 34)
3. M. caudalis lateralis - (See Plate 30)
4. M. coracobrachialis ventralis - (See Plate 19)
5. M. cutaneus cleidodorsalis - (See Plate 7)
6. M. cutaneus costohumeralis - (See Plate 16)
7. M. cutaneus pectoralis cranialis - (See Plate 20)
8. M. depressor caudae - (See Plate 22)
9. M. externus abdominis - (See Plate 25)
10. M. gluteus medius - (See Plate 29)
11. M. iliacus - (See Plate 29)
12. M. pectoralis profundus - (See Plate 21)
13. M. pectoralis superficialis - (See Plate 20)
14. M. rhomboideus - (See Plate 18)
15. M. sartorius - (See Plate 32)
16. M. scapulohumeralis minimus - (See Plate 19)
17. M. semimembranosus - (See Plate 34)
18. M. semitendinosus - (See Plate 33)
19. M. serratus dorsalis - (See Plate 19)
20. M. serratus magnus - (See Plate 18)
21. M. teres - (See Plate 17)
22. M. trapezius - (See Plate 18)
23. M. vastus internus - (See Plate 35)
24. M. vastus medialis - (See Plate 32)

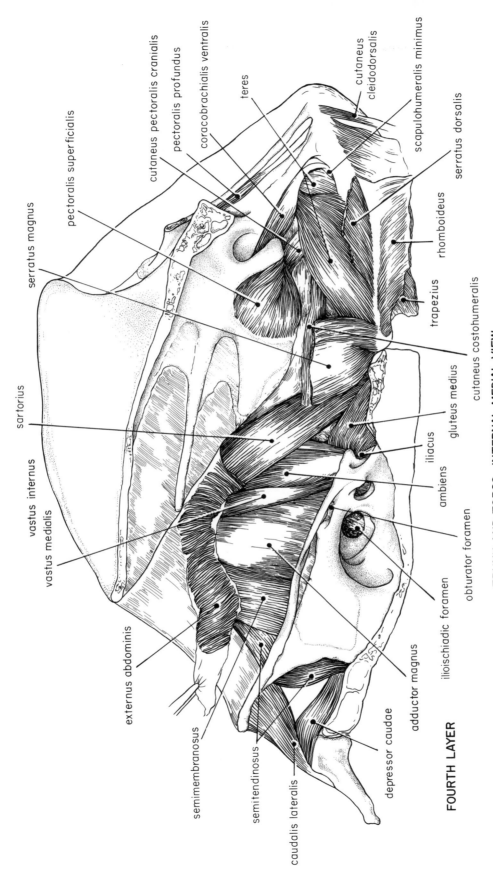

cutaneus pectoralis cranialis

pectoralis profundus

coracobrachialis ventralis

teres

cutaneus cleidodorsalis

scapulohumeralis minimus

serratus dorsalis

rhomboideus

cutaneus pectoralis superficialis

serratus magnus

trapezius

cutaneus costohumeralis

sartorius

gluteus medius

iliacus

vastus internus

ambiens

vastus medialis

obturator foramen

externus abdominis

adductor magnus

ilioischiadic foramen

semimembranosus

depressor caudae

semitendinosus

caudalis lateralis

FOURTH LAYER

TRUNK AND TORSO – INTERNAL MEDIAL VIEW

PLATE 26

Plate 27   Pelvic and Tail Muscles   Dorsal View

<u>Superficial and Second Layers</u>
  1. <u>M</u>. <u>depressor</u> <u>caudae</u> - (See Plate 22)
  2. <u>M</u>. <u>depressor</u> <u>rectricum</u> - (See Plate 22)
  3. <u>M</u>. <u>gluteus</u> <u>medius</u> - (See Plate 29)

  4. <u>M</u>. <u>gluteus</u> <u>primus</u>, large superficial gluteal muscle
      FORM AND RELATIONSHIPS: broad, flat, fan-shaped and composed of two
          divisions: a cranial fan, <u>tensor</u> <u>fascia</u> <u>latae</u> and caudal fan, <u>biceps</u>
          <u>femoris</u>. Most superficial of the lateral thigh muscles and overlies
          the <u>gluteus</u> <u>medius</u>, <u>gluteus</u> <u>minimus</u>, <u>gluteus</u> <u>superficialis</u>, <u>extensor</u>
          <u>femoris</u> and <u>biceps</u> <u>flexor</u> <u>cruris</u>.
      ORIGIN: ilium, dorsocranial crest by <u>tensor</u> <u>fascia</u> <u>latae</u> and dorsal
          crest by <u>biceps</u> <u>femoris</u>; originating fascia of the cranial fan, <u>tensor</u>
          <u>fascia</u> <u>latae</u>, is extensive and passes over the <u>gluteus</u> <u>medius</u> while the
          fascia of the caudal fan, <u>biceps</u> <u>femoris</u>, is short with fibers coming
          almost to the point of origin.
      INSERTION: tibial aponeurosis, by fascia extending from both the cranial
          and caudal fan.
      ACTION: cranial fan of <u>tensor</u> <u>fascia</u> <u>latae</u> draws thigh cranially with
          slight abduction, and the caudal fan of <u>biceps</u> <u>femoris</u> draws thigh
          caudally.

  5. <u>M</u>. <u>gluteus</u> <u>superficialis</u> - (See Plate 29)

  6. <u>M</u>. <u>levator</u> <u>caudae</u>, levator of the tail
      FORM AND RELATIONSHIPS: composed of six fasciculi not easily separated;
          deep to skin; superficial to <u>levator</u> <u>rectricum</u>, <u>interspinales</u> <u>caudae</u>,
          the sacrum, dorsal surface, the ilium, medial surface of dorsocaudal
          convex surface.
      ORIGIN: ilium, synsacral border; synsacral vertebrae, transverse
          processes, by fibers.
      INSERTION: caudal vertebrae, dorsal processes, by tendons.
      ACTION: elevates caudal vertebrae.

  7. <u>M</u>. <u>levator</u> <u>rectricum</u>, levator of the retricis
      FORM AND RELATIONSHIPS: triangular; flat; deep to skin, <u>levator</u> <u>caudae</u>,
          superficial to <u>depressor</u> <u>caudae</u>, <u>lateralis</u> <u>rectricum</u>.
      ORIGIN: caudal vertebra two, proximocaudal aspect of transverse process
          by fibers.
      INSERTION: rectricis two to five, at bases by sheath-like tendons.
      ACTION: elevates caudal rectrix.

  8. <u>M</u>. <u>longissimus</u> <u>dorsi</u> - (See Plate 15)
  9. <u>M</u>. <u>sartorius</u> - (See Plate 32)
 10. <u>M</u>. <u>semitendinosus</u> - (See Plate 33)

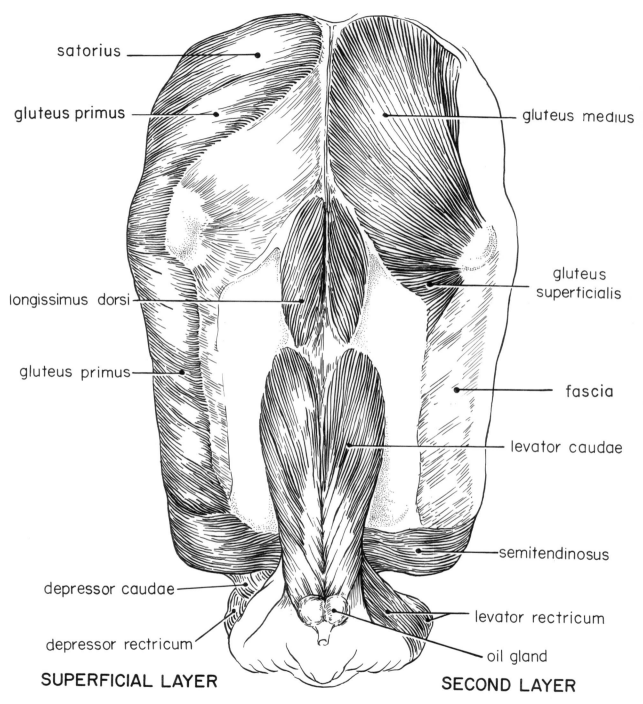

satorius

gluteus primus

gluteus medius

longissimus dorsi

gluteus superticialis

gluteus primus

fascia

levator caudae

semitendinosus

depressor caudae

depressor rectricum

levator rectricum

oil gland

SUPERFICIAL LAYER

SECOND LAYER

PELVIS AND TAIL—DORSAL VIEW
PLATE 27

Plate 28   Tail   Dorsal View

Third Layer

1. M. interspinales caudales, the caudal interspinals
   FORM AND RELATIONSHIPS: five, very small; deep to levator caudae;
     superficial to dorsal surface of caudal vertebrae.
   ORIGIN: caudal vertebrae (except pygostyle), caudal aspect of spinous
     process, by fibers.
   INSERTION: caudal vertebrae 2, including pygostyle, cranial face of
     spinous processes, by fibers.
   ACTION: elevates caudal vertebrae.

2. M. levator caudae - (See Plate 27)
3. M. levator rectricum - (See Plate 27)

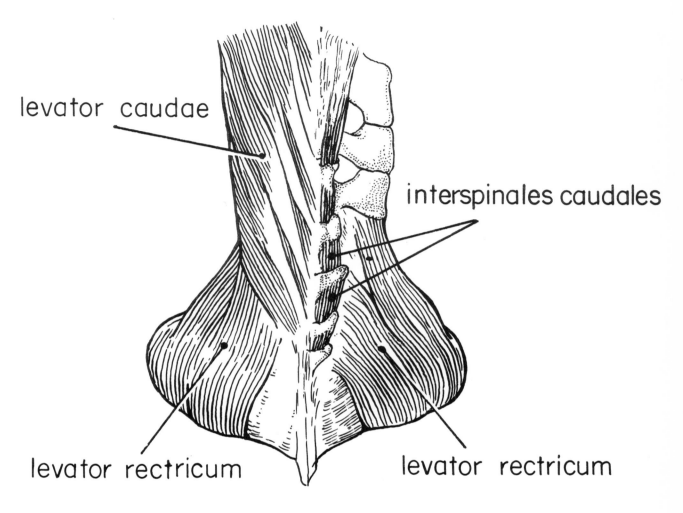

levator caudae

interspinales caudales

levator rectricum

levator rectricum

THIRD LAYER   **FOURTH LAYER**

TAIL – DORSAL VIEW
PLATE 28

Plate 29   Pelvic and Tail Muscles   Dorsal View

Third and Fourth Layers
  1. M. basirectricales - (See Plate 20)
  2. M. depressor caudae - (See Plate 22)
  3. M. depressor rectricum - (See Plate 22)

  4. M. gluteus medius, median gluteal muscle
       FORM AND RELATIONSHIPS: thick, oval-shaped; occupies cranial concave
         surface of ilium and is deep to the skin, cranial fan of gluteus
         primus, proximal two-thirds of the sartorius.
       ORIGIN: ilium, cranial concave surface, by fibers.
       INSERTION: femur lateral ridge of greater trochanter and cranioproximal
         aspect of the biceps flexor cruris by fascia.
       ACTION: extends thigh.

  5. M. gluteus minimus, lesser gluteal muscle
       FORM AND RELATIONSHIPS: flat, fan-shaped; deep to gluteus medius,
         crureus, sartorius, and cranial fan of the gluteus primus and
         superficial to ventral region of the ilium.
       ORIGIN: ilium entire ventral region of the concavity by fibers.
       INSERTION: femur trochanteric ridge laterally, base of the greater
         trochanter by tendinous fascia.
       ACTION: extends thigh.

  6. M. gluteus superficialis, superficial gluteal muscle
       FORM AND RELATIONSHIPS: small fan-shaped; deep to gluteus primus and
         superficial to gluteus medius.
       ORIGIN: ilium, dorsolateral crest just caudal to the acetabulum and
         cranial to the ilioischiadic foramen by fibers.
       INSERTION: femur lateral protuberance just distal to the greater
         trochanter, by a tendon.
       ACTION: together with other gluteal muscles aids in extension of thigh.

  7. M. iliacus, the iliacus
       FORM AND RELATIONSHIPS: fan-shaped, small; deep to gluteus medius and
         superficial to gluteus minimus.
       ORIGIN: pectineal notch by fibers.
       INSERTION: femur, tubercle on lateral surface of the greater
         trochanteric ridge, by fascia.
       ACTION: rotates thigh laterally.

  8. M. ischiofemoralis minimus - (See Plate 33)
  9. M. levator rectricum - (See Plate 27)
 10. M. sartorius - (See Plate 32)
 11. M. semitendinosus - (See Plate 33)

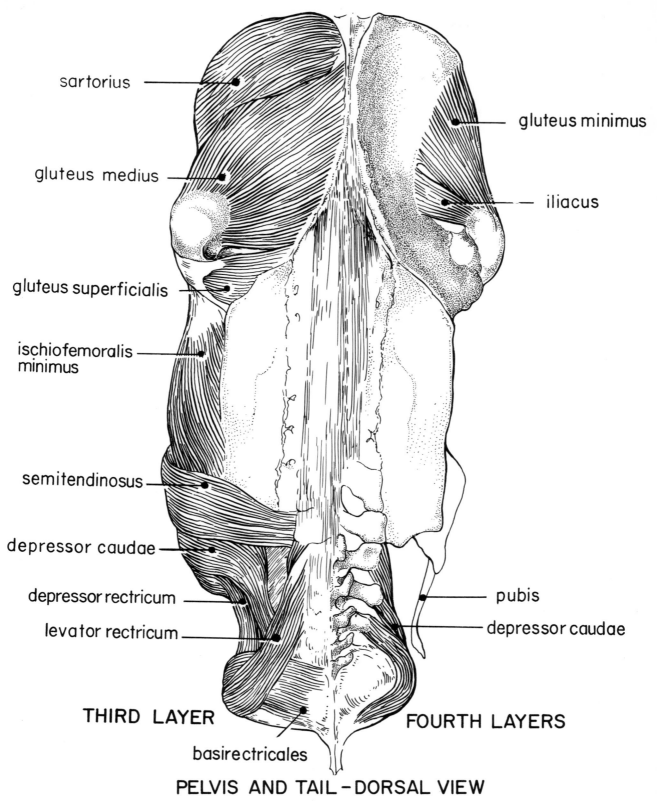

sartorius

gluteus minimus

gluteus medius

iliacus

gluteus superficialis

ischiofemoralis
minimus

semitendinosus

depressor caudae

depressor rectricum

pubis

levator rectricum

depressor caudae

THIRD LAYER

FOURTH LAYERS

basirectricales

PELVIS AND TAIL-DORSAL VIEW
PLATE 29

Plate 30   Tail   Ventral View

Superficial Layer

1. M. caudalis lateralis, lateral tail muscle
   FORM AND RELATIONSHIPS: flat and broad; deep to depressor rectricum, eversor urodeum; superficial to depressor caudae and sphincter ani.
   ORIGIN: pubis, lateral border; ischium, caudoventral border, by fibers.
   INSERTION: major undercoverts, fascia; pygostyle, caudal border, by fibers.
   ACTION: depresses and draws caudal vertebra laterally.

2. M. depressor caudae - (See Plate 22)
3. M. depressor rectricum - (See Plate 22)

4. M. eversor urodeum, the eversor of the urodeum
   FORM AND RELATIONSHIPS: string-like, thin; deep to skin, depressor rectricum, transversus perinei; superficial to fascia of perineum.
   ORIGIN: major undercoverts, fascia, by fascia.
   INSERTION: deep perineal fascia (ventral to anus) by fibers.
   ACTION: spreads ventral floor of the anus bringing about eversion of the copulatory palps.

5. M. transversus perinei, the transverse muscle of the perineum
   FORM AND RELATIONSHIPS: sphincter-like, broad and thin; deep to skin, sphincter ani; superficial to eversor urodeum, deep perineal fascia.
   ORIGIN: ischium and pubis, caudal border, by fascia.
   INSERTION: median raphe formed by fascia from fibers of the two halves of this muscle; fascia at the ventral anal opening.
   ACTION: compresses cloaca.

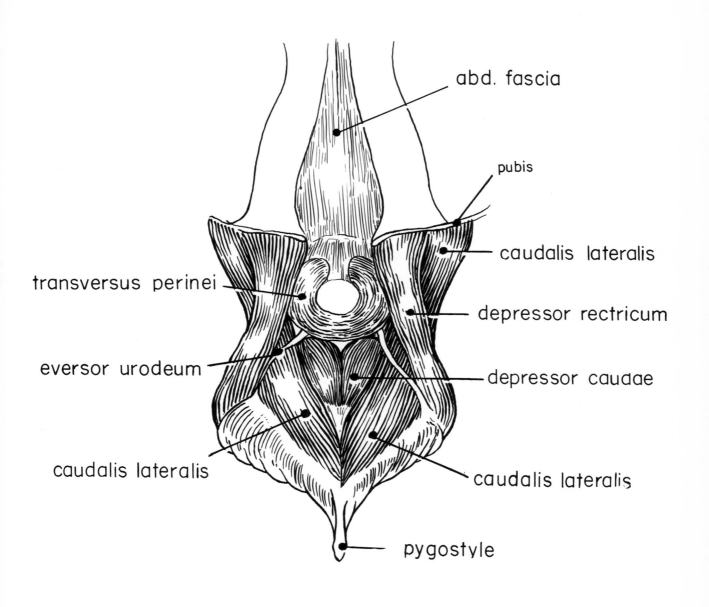

abd. fascia

pubis

caudalis lateralis

transversus perinei

depressor rectricum

eversor urodeum

depressor caudae

caudalis lateralis

caudalis lateralis

pygostyle

TAIL –VENTRAL VIEW, SUPERFICIAL LAYER
PLATE 30

Plate 31   Tail   Ventral View

Second and Deep Layers
   1. M. caudalis lateralis - (See Plate 30)
   2. M. depressor caudae - (See Plate 22)
   3. M. depressor rectricum - (See Plate 22)
   4. M. eversor urodeum - (See Plate 30)
   5. M. levator rectricum - (See Plate 27)
   6. M. transversus perinei - (See Plate 30)

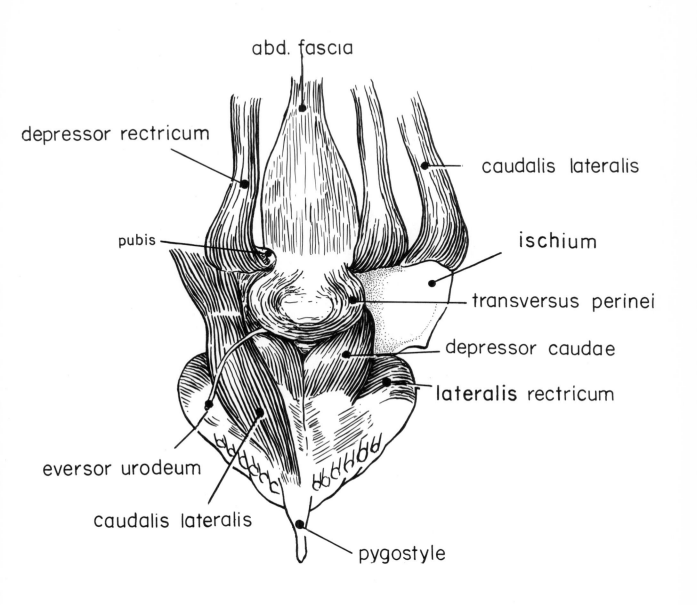

abd. fascia

depressor rectricum

caudalis lateralis

pubis

ischium

transversus perinei

depressor caudae

lateralis rectricum

eversor urodeum

caudalis lateralis

pygostyle

TAIL – VENTRAL VIEW, SECOND AND DEEP LAYERS
PLATE 31

Plate 32   Left Leg (femur)   Lateral View

<u>Superficial Layer</u>

1. <u>M</u>. <u>biceps</u> <u>flexor</u> <u>cruris</u>, two-headed flexor of the thigh
     FORM AND RELATIONSHIPS: broad, flat, triangular; superficial to
         <u>ischiofemoralis</u> <u>minimus</u>, <u>semimembranosus</u>, <u>adductor</u> <u>longus</u>, <u>adductor</u>
         <u>magnus</u>, <u>semitendinosus</u> <u>accessorius</u>, and caudal to the <u>vastus</u> <u>externus</u>.
     ORIGIN: ilium, caudal crest, and ischium, dorsal region along a narrow
         area.
     INSERTION: fibula, lateral protuberance; by a tendon which passes
         through the biceps flexor cruris sling (ligament).
     ACTION: flexes tibiotarsus.

2. <u>M</u>. <u>crureus</u> - (See <u>Extensor</u> <u>Femoris</u> - Plate 32)

3. <u>M</u>. <u>extensor</u> <u>femoris</u>, extensor of the thigh
     FORM AND RELATIONSHIPS: thick and triangular; formed by four indis-
         tinctly separate fasciculi; <u>crureus</u>, <u>subcrureus</u>, <u>vastus</u> <u>internus</u>, and
         <u>vastus</u> <u>externus</u>; deep to the <u>sartorius</u> and superficial to the femur,
         <u>ambiens</u> and abdominal muscles.
     ORIGIN: femur, lateral tuberosity at the base of the greater trochanter,
         by fibers from the common head of the <u>vastus</u> <u>externus</u> and <u>crureus</u>;
         middle two-thirds of the shaft, by fibers from the <u>vastus</u> <u>externus</u>;
         medial and cranial surface of the greater trochanter by fibers, of
         the <u>vastus</u> <u>internus</u>; distal half of the lateral surface, by fibers
         from the <u>subcrureus</u>.
     INSERTION: fascia of the <u>gluteus</u> <u>primus</u> by fibers from the <u>crureus</u>;
         tibial aponeurosis by fascia from <u>vastus</u> <u>externus</u> in common with the
         inserting tendon of the <u>subcrureus</u>; tibial aponeurosis and patella by
         fascia and fibers from <u>vastus</u> <u>internus</u> and <u>crureus</u>; tibial aponeurosis
         by a tendon from the <u>subcrureus</u> in common with fascia from the <u>vastus</u>
         <u>externus</u>.
     ACTION: extends tibiotarsus.

4. <u>M</u>. <u>flexor</u> <u>digitorum</u> <u>pedis</u> <u>profundus</u> - (See Plate 40)
5. <u>M</u>. <u>flexor</u> <u>digitorum</u> <u>pedis</u> <u>superficialis</u> - (See Plate 42)
6. <u>M</u>. <u>flexor</u> <u>hallucis</u> <u>longus</u> - (See Plate 37)
7. <u>M</u>. <u>gastrocnemius</u> <u>caput</u> <u>mediale</u> - (See Plate 41)
8. <u>M</u>. <u>gluteus</u> <u>medius</u> - (See Plate 29)
9. <u>M</u>. <u>gluteus</u> <u>minimus</u> - (See Plate 29)
10. <u>M</u>. <u>gluteus</u> <u>primus</u> - (See Plate 27)
11. <u>M</u>. <u>ischiofemoralis</u> <u>minimus</u> - (See Plate 33)

12. <u>M</u>. <u>sartorius</u>, sartorius
     FORM AND RELATIONSHIPS: straplike, long; most cranial of thigh muscles;
         deep to the skin and tendon of the <u>ambiens</u>; superficial to abdominal
         muscles; and <u>sacrolumbalis</u>, <u>crureus</u>, <u>gluteus</u> <u>medius</u>, cranial head of
         the <u>gastrocnemius</u>.
     ORIGIN: ilium, from cranial concavity and dorsal part of cranial
         ridge by fibers.
     INSERTION: tibiotarsus, by fascia into tibial aponeurosis and cranial
         border of the rotular ridge; in common with inserting fascia of <u>vastus</u>
         <u>internus</u>.
     ACTION: draws thigh cranially; abducts thigh slightly and extends
         tibiotarsus.

13. <u>M</u>. <u>semitendinosus</u> - (See Plate 33)

14. M. *tibialis cranialis* - (See Plate 38)
15. M. *vastus externus* - (See *Extensor Femoris* - Plate 32)

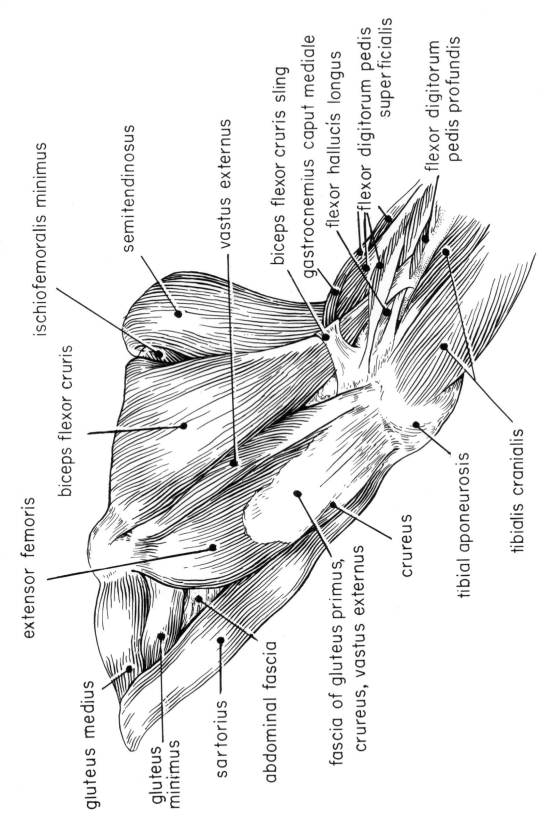

ischiofemoralis minimus

semitendinosus

vastus externus

biceps flexor cruris sling

gastrocnemius caput mediale

flexor hallucis longus

flexor digitorum pedis superficialis

flexor digitorum pedis profundis

extensor femoris

biceps flexor cruris

gluteus medius

gluteus minimus

sartorius

abdominal fascia

fascia of gluteus primus, crureus, vastus externus

crureus

tibial aponeurosis

tibialis cranialis

SUPERFICIAL LAYER

LEG (FEMUR)-LEFT-LATERAL VIEW
PLATE 32

Plate 33   Left Leg (femur)   Lateral View

Second Layer
  1. M. adductor longus - (See Plate 35)
  2. M. adductor magnus - (See Plate 34)
  3. M. crureus - (See Extensor Femoris - Plate 32)
  4. M. extensor digitorum pedis longus - (See Plate 39)
  5. M. flexor digitorum pedis profundus - (See Plate 40)
  6. M. flexor digitorum pedis superficialis - (See Plate 42)
  7. M. gastrocnemius - (See Caput Mediale - Plate 41)
  8. M. gluteus medius - (See Plate 29)
  9. M. gluteus minimus - (See Plate 29)
 10. M. gluteus superficialis - (See Plate 29)

 11. M. ischiofemoralis minimus, lesser ischiofemoral muscle
       FORM AND RELATIONSHIPS: fan-shaped and flat; deep to biceps flexor
       cruris, vastus externus and superficial to obturator externus and
       ischium.
       ORIGIN: ischium, caudodorsal aspect and caudal margin.
       INSERTION: femur, greater trochanter at the base caudally.
       ACTION: draws thigh caudally.

 12. M. obturator externus - (See Plate 34)
 13. M. sartorius - (See Plate 32)
 14. M. semimembranosus - (See Plate 34)

 15. M. semitendinosus, the semitendinosus
       FORM AND RELATIONSHIPS: straplike, thick; deep to the skin, biceps
       flexor cruris, vastus externus, and flexor hallucis longus.
       ORIGIN: ilium, caudal crest, most caudal aspect by fibers.
       INSERTION: tibiotarsus, shaft and in common with inserting tendinosus
       fascia of the semimembranosus, also by fascia to the proximomedial
       aspect of the gastrocnemius (caput mediale).
       ACTION: draws thigh caudally and aids in flexing shank.

 16. M. semitendinosus accessorius, accessory to the semitendinous muscle
       FORM AND RELATIONSHIPS: broad and flat; deep to biceps flexor cruris,
       extensor femoris and superficial to adductor magnus and semi-
       membranosus.
       ORIGIN: femur, caudodistal fourth by fibers.
       INSERTION: raphe of semitendinosus by fibers.
       ACTION: draws thigh caudally with aid of semitendinosus.

 17. M. subcrureus - (See Extensor Femoris - Plate 32)
 18. M. vastus externus - (See Extensor Femoris - Plate 32)

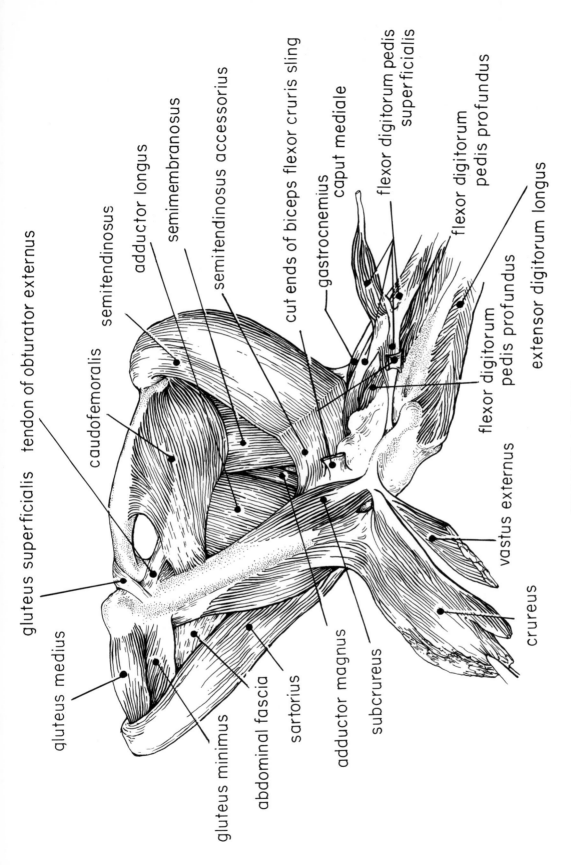

gluteus superficialis

tendon of obturator externus

semitendinosus

caudofemoralis

adductor longus

semimembranosus

semitendinosus accessorius

cut ends of biceps flexor cruris sling

gastrocnemius

caput mediale

flexor digitorum pedis superficialis

flexor digitorum pedis profundus

extensor digitorum longus

flexor digitorum pedis profundus

vastus externus

crureus

subcrureus

adductor magnus

sartorius

abdominal fascia

gluteus minimus

gluteus medius

SECOND LAYER

LEG (FEMUR)–LEFT–LATERAL VIEW
PLATE 33

Plate 34   Left Leg (femur)   Medial View

<u>Superficial Layer</u>
1. <u>M</u>. <u>adductor</u> <u>longus</u> - (See Plate 35)

2. <u>M</u>. <u>adductor</u> <u>magnus</u>, large adductor muscle
   FORM AND RELATIONSHIPS: fan-shaped, thick and broad (cranial to
      semimembranosus) and superficial to <u>ischiofemoralis</u> <u>minimus</u>, <u>biceps</u>
      <u>flexor</u> <u>cruris</u>, <u>adductor</u> <u>longus</u>, and <u>semitendinosus</u> <u>accessorius</u>.
   ORIGIN: pubis, lateral and dorsal surface, by fascia.
   INSERTION: femur, medial condyle, by fibers.
   ACTION: adducts thigh.

3. <u>M</u>. <u>ambiens</u>, perching muscle
   FORM AND RELATIONSHIPS: flat, thin, small; deep to <u>sartorius</u> and <u>rectus</u>
      <u>abdominus</u>; superficial to <u>vastus</u> <u>internus</u>.
   ORIGIN: pubis, ventral and cranial border.
   INSERTION: originating tendon of <u>flexor</u> <u>digiti</u> <u>terti</u> <u>perforatus</u> after
      passing through pectineal groove of patella and the tibial aponeurosis.
   ACTION: aids in flexing digits II, III, and IV.

4. <u>M</u>. <u>biceps</u> <u>flexor</u> <u>cruris</u> - (See Plate 32)
5. <u>M</u>. <u>crureus</u> - (See <u>Extensor</u> <u>Femoris</u> - Plate 32)
6. <u>M</u>. <u>gastrocnemius</u> <u>caput</u> <u>caudale</u> - (See Plate 41)
7. <u>M</u>. <u>gastrocnemius</u> <u>caput</u> <u>craniale</u> - (See Plate 41)

8. <u>M</u>. <u>gemellus</u>, gemellus muscle
   FORM AND RELATIONSHIPS: small, straplike, superficial to the cranial
      portion of the pubis and acetabulum and cranial to <u>adductor</u> <u>magnus</u>,
      <u>adductor</u> <u>longus</u> and tendon of <u>obturator</u> <u>internus</u>.
   ORIGIN: pubis, dorsal surface just cranial to obturator foramen.
   INSERTION: subtrochanteric fossa, by fibers.
   ACTION: aids in adduction of thigh.

9. <u>M</u>. <u>gluteus</u> <u>medius</u> - (See Plate 29)
10. <u>M</u>. <u>gluteus</u> <u>minimus</u> - (See Plate 29)
11. <u>M</u>. <u>gluteus</u> <u>superficialis</u> - (See Plate 29)
12. <u>M</u>. <u>iliacus</u> - (See Plate 29)
13. <u>M</u>. <u>ischiofemoralis</u> <u>minimus</u> - (See Plate 33)

14. <u>M</u>. <u>obturator</u> <u>externus</u>, external obturator
   FORM AND RELATIONSHIPS: broad and flat; deep to <u>ischiofemoralis</u>
      <u>minimus</u>, and superficial to inserting tendon of <u>obturator</u> <u>internus</u>,
      and ischium.
   ORIGIN: ischium, caudal to ilioischiatic foramen, by fibers.
   INSERTION: femur, greater trochanter, caudal lateral face at the base.
   ACTION: draws thigh caudally.

15. <u>M</u>. <u>obturator</u> <u>internus</u> - (See Plate 23)
16. <u>M</u>. <u>sartorius</u> - (See Plate 32)

17. <u>M</u>. <u>semimembranosus</u>, semimembranosus muscle
   FORM AND RELATIONSHIPS: slightly triangular, broad and flat, deep to
      <u>biceps</u> <u>flexor</u> <u>cruris</u>, <u>semitendinosus</u>, <u>semitendinosus</u> <u>accessorius</u>,
      <u>gastrocnemius</u> and superficial to <u>rectus</u> <u>abdominus</u>.
   ORIGIN: ischium (middle third), ventral border, by fibers.
   INSERTION: tibiotarsus, proximomedial aspect in common with inserting
      fascia of the <u>semitendinosus</u> <u>accessorius</u>.
   ACTION: draws thigh caudally and flexes thigh.

18. <u>M</u>. <u>semitendinosus</u> - (See Plate 33)
19. <u>M</u>. <u>vastus internus</u> - (See <u>Extensor Femoris</u> - Plate 32)
20. <u>M</u>. <u>vastus medialis</u> - (See <u>Extensor Femoris</u> - Plate 32)

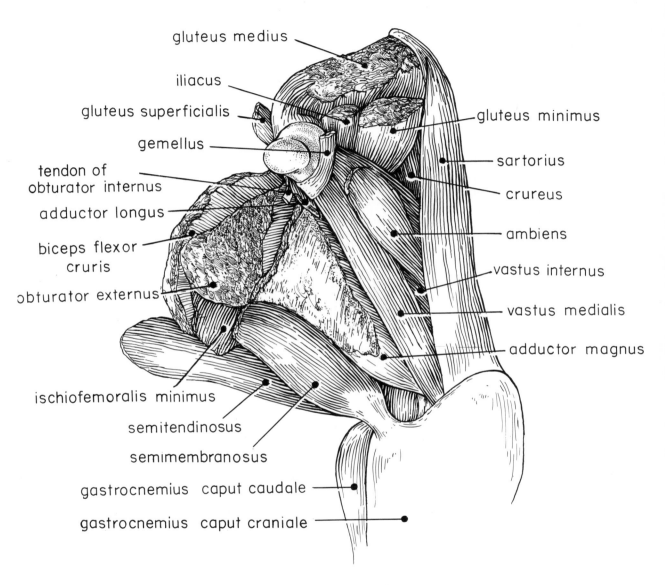

gluteus medius

iliacus

gluteus superficialis

gemellus

tendon of
obturator internus

adductor longus

biceps flexor
cruris

obturator externus

gluteus minimus

sartorius

crureus

ambiens

vastus internus

vastus medialis

adductor magnus

ischiofemoralis minimus

semitendinosus

semimembranosus

gastrocnemius caput caudale

gastrocnemius caput craniale

SUPERFICIAL LAYER

LEG (FEMUR) – LEFT – MEDIAL VIEW
PLATE 34

Plate 35   Left Leg (femur)   Medial View

Second Layer

1. M. adductor longus, long adductor muscle
   FORM AND RELATIONSHIPS: broad and straplike; deep to vastus externus,
      semitendinosus accessorius, biceps flexor cruris, obturator externus,
      ischiofemoralis minimus and superficial to adductor magnus.
   ORIGIN: ischium, ventral border, cranial third, by fibers.
   INSERTION: femur, distocaudal two-thirds.
   ACTION: adducts thigh and draws it slightly caudalward.

2. M. biceps flexor cruris - (See Plate 32)
3. M. crureus - (See Extensor Femoris - Plate 32)
4. M. flexor digitorum pedis profundus - (See Plate 40)
5. M. flexor digitorum pedis superficialis - (See Plate 42)
6. M. gluteus medius - (See Plate 29)
7. M. gluteus minimus - (See Plate 29)
8. M. gluteus primus - (See Plate 27)
9. M. iliacus - (See Plate 29)
10. M. ischiofemoralis minimus - (See Plate 29)
11. M. peroneus longus - (See Plate 37)
12. M. semitendinosus - (See Plate 33)
13. M. semitendinosus accessorius - (See Plate 33)
14. M. tibialis caudalis - (See Plate 42)
15. M. tibialis cranialis - (See Plate 38)
16. M. vastus internus - (See Extensor Femoris - Plate 32)

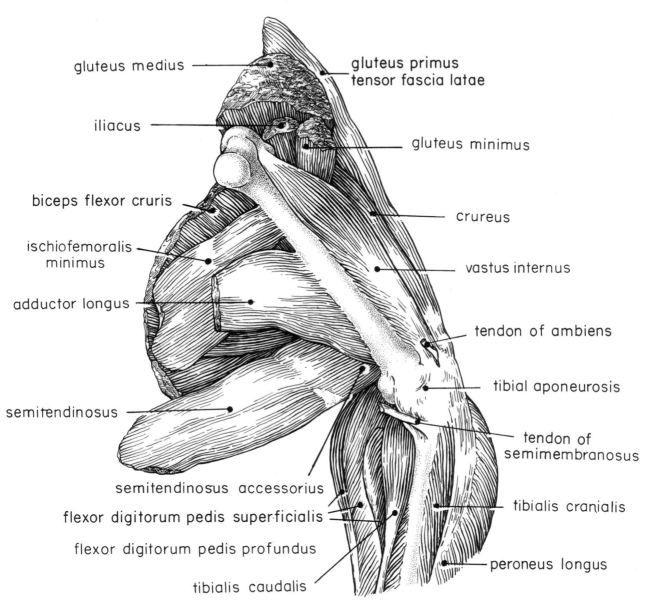

gluteus medius

gluteus primus
tensor fascia latae

iliacus

gluteus minimus

biceps flexor cruris

crureus

ischiofemoralis
minimus

vastus internus

adductor longus

tendon of ambiens

tibial aponeurosis

semitendinosus

tendon of
semimembranosus

semitendinosus accessorius

tibialis cranialis

flexor digitorum pedis superficialis

flexor digitorum pedis profundus

peroneus longus

tibialis caudalis

SECOND LAYER

LEG (FEMUR) - LEFT - MEDIAL VIEW
PLATE 35

Plate 36   Left Leg (femur)   Medial View

Third Layer
   1. M. biceps flexor cruris - (See Plate 32)
   2. M. crureus - (See Extensor Femoris - Plate 32)
   3. M. flexor digitorum pedis profundus - (See Plate 40)
   4. M. flexor digitorum pedis superficialis - (See Plate 42)
   5. M. gastrocnemius caput caudale -(See Plate 41)
   6. M. gluteus medius - (See Plate 29)
   7. M. gluteus minimus - (See Plate 29)
   8. M. gluteus primus - (See Plate 27)
   9. M. iliacus - (See Plate 29)
  10. M. tibialis cranialis - (See Plate 38)
  11. M. vastus externus - (See Extensor Femoris - Plate 32)

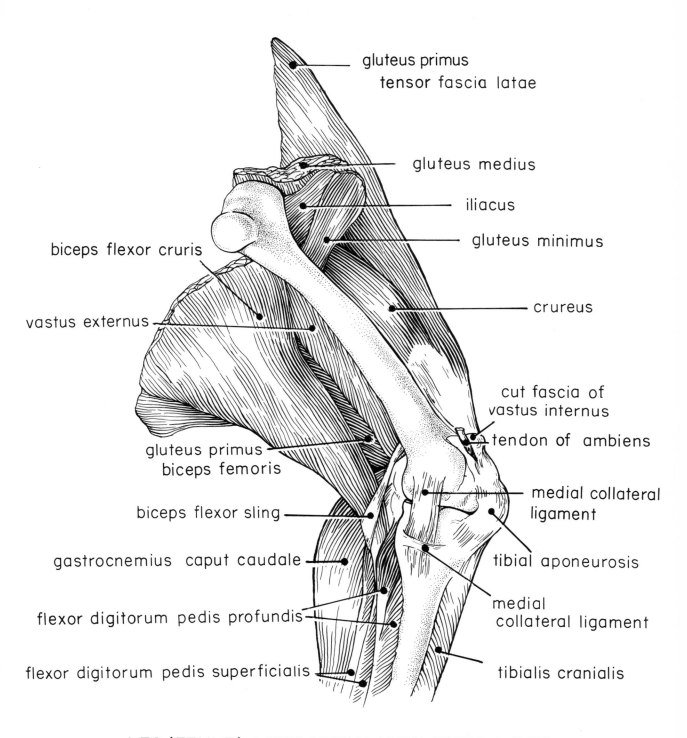

gluteus primus
tensor fascia latae

gluteus medius

iliacus

gluteus minimus

biceps flexor cruris

crureus

vastus externus

cut fascia of
vastus internus

tendon of ambiens

gluteus primus
biceps femoris

medial collateral
ligament

biceps flexor sling

tibial aponeurosis

gastrocnemius caput caudale

medial
collateral ligament

flexor digitorum pedis profundis

flexor digitorum pedis superficialis

tibialis cranialis

LEG (FEMUR)-LEFT-MEDIAL VIEW, THIRD LAYER
PLATE 36

Plate 37   Left Leg (tibiotarsus)   Lateral View

Superficial Layer
1. M. biceps flexor cruris - (See Plate 32)
2. M. flexor digiti quarti perforatus - (See Plate 42)
3. M. flexor digiti secundi perforatus et perforans - (See Plate 38)
4. M. flexor digiti terti perforatus - (See Plate 42)
5. M. flexor digiti terti perforatus et perforans - (See Plate 38)
6. M. flexor digitorum pedis profundus - (See Plate 40)

7. M. flexor hallucis longus, long flexor of the hallux
    FORM AND RELATIONSHIPS: fan-shaped, narrow; deep to flexor digitorum
       pedis superficialis and superficial to flexor digitorum pedis
       profundus.
    ORIGIN: femur, intercondylar fossa, by fibers and fascia.
    INSERTION: hallux, first phalanx, by tendinous slip, and fascia
       covering foot digits.
    ACTION: flexes and adducts hallux; aids in flexing digits II, III, IV.

8. M. gastrocnemius caput caudale - (See Plate 41)
9. M. gastrocnemius caput craniale - (See Plate 41)
10. M. gluteus primus fascia - (See Plate 27)

11. M. peroneus longus, the long peroneus
    FORM AND RELATIONSHIPS: broad, thick and tapering; deep to the skin,
       superficial to tibialis cranialis, extensor digitorum pedis longus
       and caudal to gastrocnemius caput craniale.
    ORIGIN: tibiotarsus, procnemial ridge, lateral cranial border and apex
       of the cnemial ridge by fibers.
    INSERTION: third digit, by a long tendon and in common with the tendon
       of the flexor digiti terti perforatus and to the tarsometatarsal
       capsule, by a short tendon.
    ACTION: extends tarsometatarsus and aids in flexing digits II, III, IV.

12. M. semimembranosus - (See Plate 34)
13. M. tibialis cranialis - (See Plate 38)

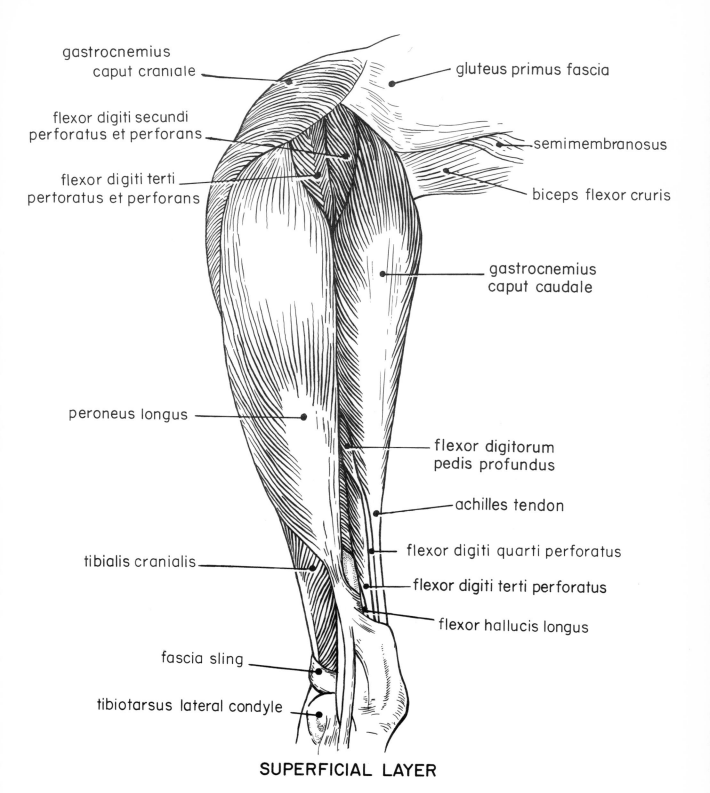

gastrocnemius
caput craniale

gluteus primus fascia

flexor digiti secundi
perforatus et perforans

semimembranosus

flexor digiti terti
perforatus et perforans

biceps flexor cruris

gastrocnemius
caput caudale

peroneus longus

flexor digitorum
pedis profundus

achilles tendon

tibialis cranialis

flexor digiti quarti perforatus

flexor digiti terti perforatus

flexor hallucis longus

fascia sling

tibiotarsus lateral condyle

SUPERFICIAL LAYER

LEG (TIBIOTARSUS)-LEFT-LATERAL VIEW
PLATE 37

Plate 38   Left Leg (tibiotarsus)   Lateral View

Second Layer
 1. M. biceps flexor cruris - (See Plate 32)
 2. M. extensor digitorum longus - (See Plate 39)
 3. M. flexor digiti quarti perforatus - (See Plate 42 - No. 6)
 4. M. flexor digiti secundi perforatus - (See Plate 42 - No. 6)

 5. M. flexor digiti secundi perforatus et perforans, the perforated and
    perforating flexor of the second digit
       FORM AND RELATIONSHIPS: flat and thin; deep to the skin; superficial to
          flexor digiti terti perforatus et perforans and inserting tendon of
          biceps flexor cruris and cranial to gastrocnemius caput caudale.
       ORIGIN: tibial aponeurosis, by fibers.
       INSERTION: by two tendinous slips which insert one on second phalanx of
          the second digit, proximolateral process, and one on proximomedial
          process.
       ACTION: flexes digit II.

 6. M. flexor digiti terti perforatus - (See Plate 42 - No. 6)

 7. M. flexor digiti terti perforatus et perforans, the perforated and
    perforating flexor of the third digit
       FORM AND RELATIONSHIPS: narrow and long; deep to the skin of the shank;
          superficial to the tibialis cranialis, extensor digitorum pedis
          longus and inserting tendon of the biceps flexor cruris, caudal to
          peroneus longus.
       ORIGIN: tibial aponeurosis and fibula, lateral protuberance, by fibers.
       INSERTION: digit III, third phalanx, laterally on the caudal
          articulating process by a tendinous slip and by the other tendinous
          slip plantarly and medially on the caudal and medial articulating
          process.
       ACTION: flexes digit III.

 8. M. flexor digitorum pedis profundus - (See Plate 41)
 9. M. flexor hallucis longus - (See Plate 37)
10. M. peroneus brevis - (See Plate 40)

11. M. tibialis cranialis, the cranial tibialis muscle
       FORM AND RELATIONSHIPS: straplike, long and thick, with two heads
          (superficial and deep heads); deep to peroneus longus and
          superficial to peroneus brevis tibiotarsus, extensor digitorum longus.
       ORIGIN: superficial head: tibiotarsus, procnemial and ecnemial ridges,
                   by fibers.
                deep head: femur, lateral epicondyle, by a tendon.
       INSERTION: tarsometatarsus, dorsally by a tendon.
       ACTION: flexes tarsometatarsus.

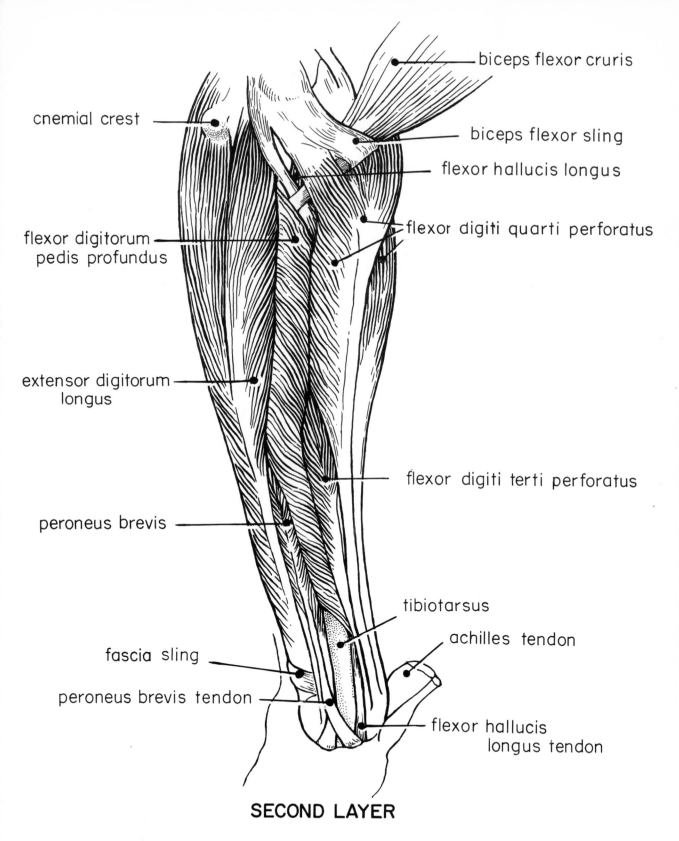

biceps flexor cruris

cnemial crest

biceps flexor sling

flexor hallucis longus

flexor digiti quarti perforatus

flexor digitorum
pedis profundus

extensor digitorum
longus

flexor digiti terti perforatus

peroneus brevis

tibiotarsus

achilles tendon

fascia sling

peroneus brevis tendon

flexor hallucis
longus tendon

SECOND LAYER

**LEG (TIBIOTARSUS) – LEFT–LATERAL VIEW
PLATE 38**

Plate 39   Left Leg (tibiotarsus)   Lateral View

Third Layer

1. M. biceps flexor cruris - (See Plate 32)

2. M. extensor digitorum pedis longus, the long extensor of the foot digits
    FORM AND RELATIONSHIPS: long and narrow with a bifurcating tendon;
        deep to tibialis cranialis; superficial to procnemial crest of
        tibiotarsus.
    ORIGIN: tibiotarsus, rotular ridge and procnemial crest lateral face.
    INSERTION: the medial tendon gives rise to three slips; the medial of
        these three slips inserts on digit II, terminal phalanx; the middle
        slip inserts on digit IV, proximomedial process of phalanx II; and the
        lateral slip inserts on digit II, phalanx I, proximolateral process
        as well as digit III, phalanx I, dorsomedial process and phalanx II
        proximodorsal process.
                The lateral tendon gives rise to two slips; the medial slip
        also bifurcates and inserts on digit III, terminal phalanx, and also
        to the proximodorsal process.
                The lateral slip bifurcates and inserts on digit IV,
        terminal phalanx, and on phalanx II proximodorsal process.
    ACTION: extends digits II, III, IV.

3. M. flexor digiti quarti perforatus - (See Plate 42)
4. M. flexor digiti terti perforatus - (See Plate 42)
5. M. flexor digitorum pedis profundus - (See Plate 40)
6. M. flexor hallucis longus - (See Plate 37)
7. M. peroneus brevis - (See Plate 40)

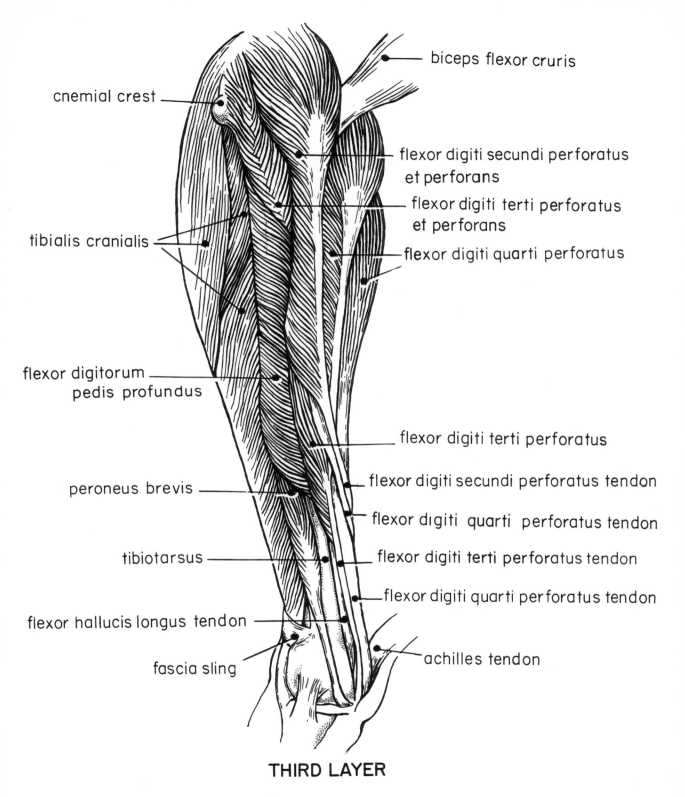

cnemial crest

biceps flexor cruris

flexor digiti secundi perforatus et perforans

flexor digiti terti perforatus et perforans

flexor digiti quarti perforatus

tibialis cranialis

flexor digitorum pedis profundus

flexor digiti terti perforatus

flexor digiti secundi perforatus tendon

flexor digiti quarti perforatus tendon

peroneus brevis

flexor digiti terti perforatus tendon

tibiotarsus

flexor digiti quarti perforatus tendon

flexor hallucis longus tendon

fascia sling

achilles tendon

THIRD LAYER

LEG (TIBIOTARSUS)–LEFT–LATERAL VIEW
PLATE 39

Plate 40   Left Leg (tibiotarsus)   Lateral View

<u>Deep Layer</u>
1. <u>M</u>. <u>extensor</u> <u>digitorum</u> <u>pedis</u> <u>longus</u> - (See Plate 39)

2. <u>M</u>. <u>flexor</u> <u>digitorum</u> <u>pedis</u> <u>profundus</u>, deep flexor of the foot digits
   FORM AND RELATIONSHIPS: flat and long with fibers converging on an
      ossified tendon; deep to <u>flexor</u> <u>hallucis</u> <u>longus</u>; superficial to
      <u>peroneus</u> <u>brevis</u>, <u>popliteus</u> and caudal face of fibula and tibiotarsus.
   ORIGIN: fibula and tibiotarsus, caudal faces, by fibers.
   INSERTION: uncinate (terminal) phalanges of digits II, III and IV,
      plantarly, by three slips from the tendon.
   ACTION: flexes digits II, III, IV.

3. <u>M</u>. <u>peroneus</u> <u>brevis</u>, short peroneus
   FORM AND RELATIONSHIPS: thin, terminating in an ossified tendon; deep
      to deep head of <u>tibialis</u> <u>cranialis</u>; superficial to <u>flexor</u> <u>digitorum</u>
      <u>pedis</u> <u>profundus</u>.
   ORIGIN: tibiotarsus and fibular stylus, distal two-thirds, by fibers.
   INSERTION: hypotarsus; by a tendon.
   ACTION: probably to hold tarsometatarsus firmly to tibiotarsus during
      flexion of the tarsometatarsus. It may aid in extension of
      tarsometatarsus.

4. <u>M</u>. <u>popliteus</u>, the popliteal
   FORM AND RELATIONSHIPS: bandlike, short; deep to <u>flexor</u> <u>digitorum</u> <u>pedis</u>
      <u>superficialis</u>, <u>flexor</u> <u>digitorum</u> <u>pedis</u> <u>profundus</u>, superficial to
      proximocaudal tenth of tibiotarsus.
   ORIGIN: fibula, head, medial aspect, by fibers.
   INSERTION: tibiotarsus, popliteal depression, by fibers.
   ACTION: adducts fibular head.

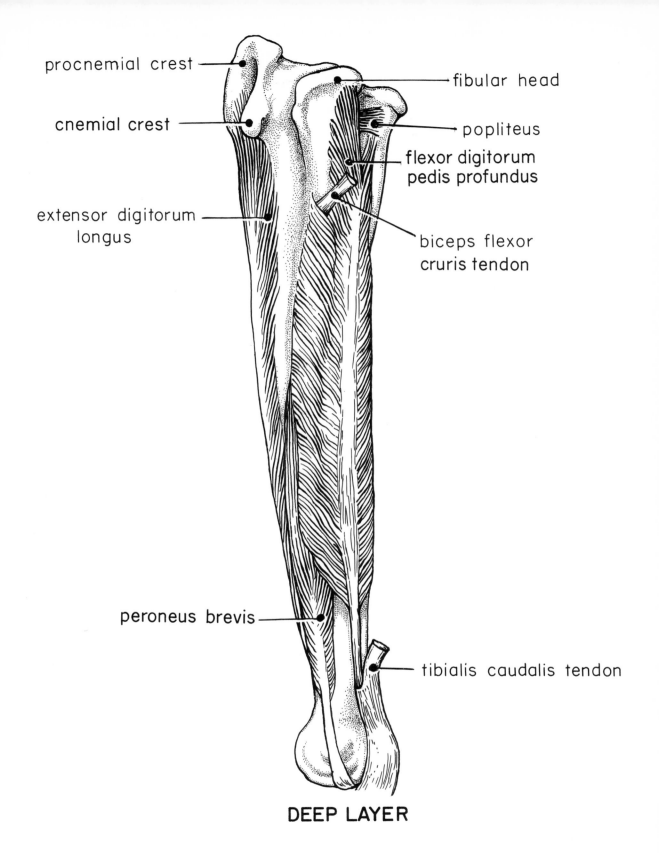

procnemial crest

cnemial crest

extensor digitorum
longus

peroneus brevis

fibular head

popliteus

flexor digitorum
pedis profundus

biceps flexor
cruris tendon

tibialis caudalis tendon

DEEP LAYER

LEG (TIBIOTARSUS) - LEFT-LATERAL VIEW
PLATE 40

Plate 41   Leg (tibiotarsus) Left   Medial View

Superficial Layer
1. M. extensor digitorum pedis longus - (See Plate 39)
2. M. flexor digitorum pedis profundus - (See Plate 40)

3. M. gastrocnemius, gastrocnemius
   FORM AND RELATIONSHIPS: largest of shank muscles and composed of three
      heads; caput caudale, caput craniale, and caput mediale. Their fibers
      end distally to form the achilles tendon.
      Caput caudale: broad, flat; deep to the skin; superficial to flexor
         digiti secundi perforatus et perforans, biceps flexor cruris,
         flexor hallucis longus, flexor digitorum pedis superficialis,
         cranial to caput mediale.
   ORIGIN: femur, lateral epicondyle, by a tendon.
   INSERTION: tarsometatarsus, plantar lateral crest, by fascia in common
      with caput mediale, and caput craniale.
   ACTION: extends tarsometatarsus.
      Caput mediale: triangular and long; deep to the skin, distal fibers
         of semimembranosus; superficial to tibialis caudalis, biceps flexor
         cruris, flexor hallucis longus, flexor digitorum pedis
         superficialis; caudal to caput craniale.
   ORIGIN: femur, medial condyle, by fascia.
   INSERTION: tarsometatarsus, ossified tendon in common with caput
      craniale by fibers.
   ACTION: extends tarsometatarsus.
      Caput craniale: broad and flat; deep to skin; superficial to
         tibialis cranialis, extensor digitorum pedis longus, tibialis
         caudalis and tibiotarsus; cranial to caput mediale.
   ORIGIN: tibial aponeurosis by fibers; tarsometatarsus, rotular ridge
      and medial face of procnemial ridge by fibers.
   INSERTION: tarsometatarsus, plantar lateral crest by fascia in common
      with caput caudale.
   ACTION: extends tarsometatarsus.

4. M. peroneus longus - (See Plate 37)

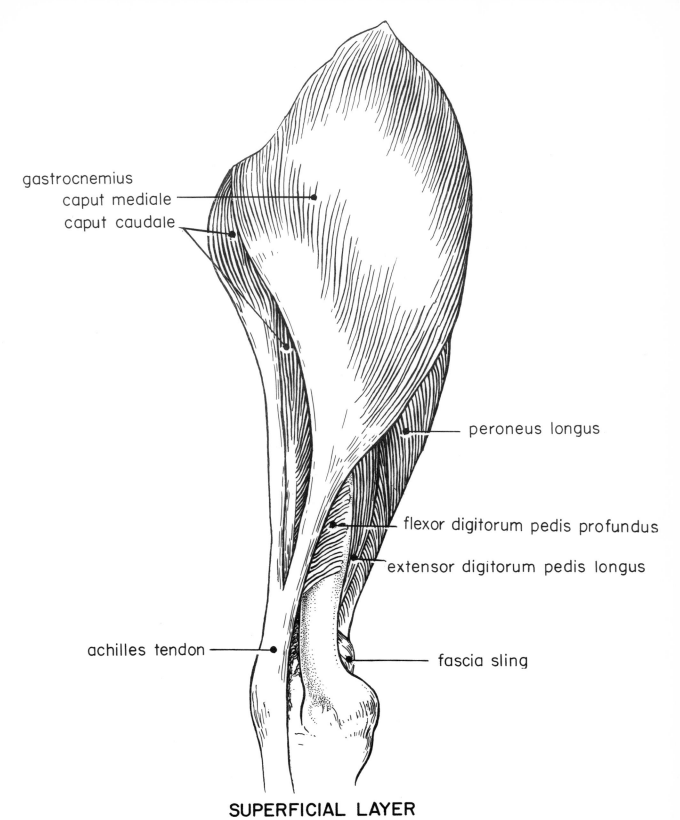

gastrocnemius
caput mediale
caput caudale

peroneus longus

flexor digitorum pedis profundus

extensor digitorum pedis longus

achilles tendon

fascia sling

SUPERFICIAL LAYER

LEG (TIBIOTARSUS)–LEFT–MEDIAL VIEW
PLATE 41

Plate 42   Leg (tibiotarsus)   Left Medial View

Second Layer
1. M. crureus - (See Extensor Femoris - Plate 32)
2. M. extensor digitorum pedis longus - (See Plate 39)
3. M. flexor digiti secundi perforatus et perforans - (See Plate 38)
4. M. flexor digiti terti perforatus et perforans - (See Plate 38)
5. M. flexor digitorum pedis profundus - (See Plate 40)

6. M. flexor digitorum pedis superficialis, superficial digital flexor of the
   foot
   FORM AND RELATIONSHIPS: a complex muscle composed of five fasciculi
      which terminate in three tendons; deep to gastrocnemius; superficial
      to flexor hallucis longus, tibialis caudalis and flexor digitorum
      pedis profundus and popliteus. Subdivisions of the superficial digital
      flexor are designated as (a) the flexor digiti perforati of the second,
      third and fourth digits. The five fasciculi are apportioned
      respectively as follows: (a) medial, (b) distal and caudal, and (c)
      proximal and lateral.
   ORIGIN:
      M. flexor digiti secundi perforatus - the medial fasciculus takes its
         origin by fibers from the proximal and caudal fasciculi.
      M. flexor digiti terti perforatus - the caudal fasciculus takes its
         origin by fibers from the proximal fasciculus. The distal
         fasciculus originates by a tendon from the lateral collateral
         ligament. This originating tendon also receives the inserting tendon
         of the ambiens.
      M. flexor digiti quarti perforatus - the proximal fasciculus arises by
         fibers and fascia from the fibular groove of the femur. The lateral
         fasciculus originates by a fascia from the belly of the proximal
         fasciculus.
   INSERTION:
      M. flexor digiti secundi perforatus - an ossified tendon of this
         fasciculus extends distally, passing through the tarsometatarsal
         capsule, and bifurcates at the first phalanx of the second digit.
         One slip of the tendon inserts on the proximolateral process of the
         first phalanx of the second digit and the second slip inserts on the
         proximomedial process of the same phalanx. M. flexor digiti secundi
         perforatus et perforans, perforates the tendon at the point of
         its bifurcation.
      M. flexor digiti terti perforatus - the fibers of both fasciculi
         terminate in a common ossified tendon which continues distally pass-
         ing through the tarsometatarsal capsule. Just distal to the
         tarsometatarsal capsule it is joined inseparably by the tendon of
         the peroneus longus. The continuing tendon bifurcates at the distal
         articulation of the first phalanx of the third digit. One slip
         inserts on the proximolateral process of the second phalanx of the
         third digit. The second slip inserts on the proximomedial process
         of the same phalanx. The tendon is perforated at its bifurcation
         by the tendon of the flexor digiti terti perforatus et perforans.
      M. flexor digiti quarti perforatus - the two fasciculi of this muscle
         terminate in an ossified tendon which continues distally and passes
         through the tarsometatarsal capsule onto the plantar surface of the
         tarsometatarsus. It trifurcates at the proximal articulation of the
         first phalanx of the fourth digit. One slip inserts on the proximo-
         lateral process of the second phalanx of the fourth digit, a second
         slip inserts on the intercondyloid process of the same phalanx and
         a third slip inserts also on the proximomedial process of the third
         phalanx of the fourth digit. At the point of trifurcation, this

flexor is perforated by one of the tendinous slips of the M. flexor digitorum pedis profundus.
    ACTION: flexes digits II, III and IV.

7. M. tibialis caudalis, caudal tibialis muscle
    FORM AND RELATIONSHIPS: cone-shape and small; deep lateral and cranial to caput craniale of gastrocnemius, flexor digitorum pedis superficialis and superficial to proximocaudal aspect of tibiotarsus.
    ORIGIN: tibiotarsus, at base of rotular ridge.
    INSERTION: tibial cartilage and fascia and capsule caudal to the tibiotarsus--tarsometatarsus articulation by a tendon.
    ACTION: extends tarsometatarsus.

8. M. tibialis cranialis - (See Plate 38)
9. M. vastus internus - (See Extensor Femoris - Plate 35)

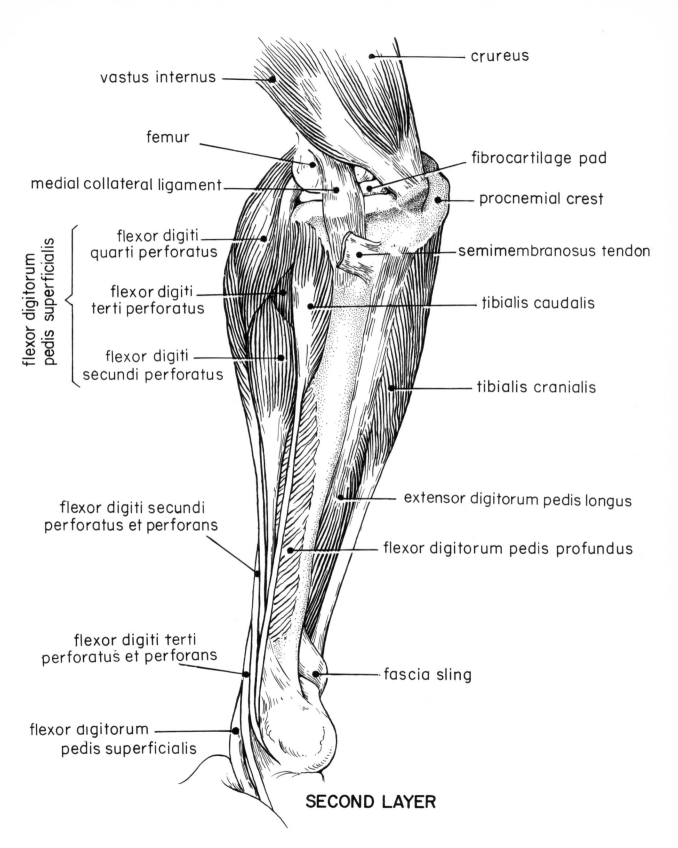

crureus

vastus internus

femur

medial collateral ligament

flexor digitorum pedis superficialis
- flexor digiti quarti perforatus
- flexor digiti terti perforatus
- flexor digiti secundi perforatus

fibrocartilage pad

procnemial crest

semimembranosus tendon

tibialis caudalis

tibialis cranialis

flexor digiti secundi perforatus et perforans

extensor digitorum pedis longus

flexor digitorum pedis profundus

flexor digiti terti perforatus et perforans

fascia sling

flexor digitorum pedis superficialis

SECOND LAYER

LEG (TIBIOTARSUS)-LEFT-MEDIAL VIEW
PLATE 42

Plate 43   Leg (tibiotarsus) Left   Medial View

Third Layer
1. M. extensor digitorum pedis longus - (See Plate 39)
2. M. flexor digitorum pedis profundus - (See Plate 40)
3. M. popliteus - (See Plate 40)

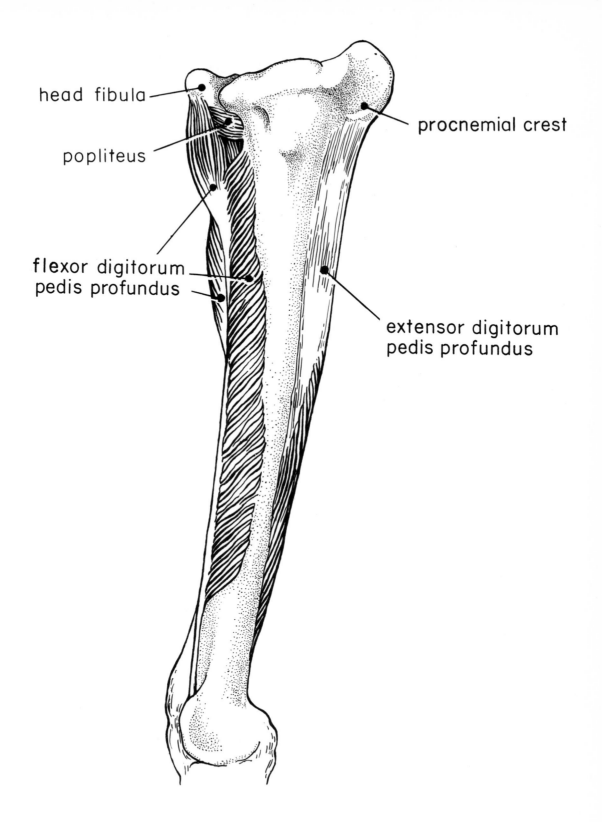

head fibula

popliteus

flexor digitorum
pedis profundus

procnemial crest

extensor digitorum
pedis profundus

LEG (TIBIOTARSUS)—LEFT—MEDIAL VIEW   THIRD LAYER
PLATE 43

Plate 44   Leg (tarsometatarsus and foot) Left   Lateral View

Superficial Layer

1. M. abductor digiti quarti pedis, abductor of the fourth foot digit
   FORM AND RELATIONSHIPS: two bellies separated by tendon; deep to tendon
      of flexor digitorum pedis profundus; superficial to the plantar surface
      of the tarsometatarsus.
   ORIGIN: tarsometatarsus, hypotarsus plantar surface by fibers and third
      trochlea, plantar surface by fibers.
   INSERTION: digit IV phalanx I, proximolateral surface, by a tendon.
   ACTION: abducts digit IV.

2. M. flexor digiti quarti perforatus - (See Plate 42)
3. M. flexor digiti secundi perforatus et perforans - (See Plate 38)
4. M. flexor digiti terti perforatus - (See Plate 42)
5. M. flexor digiti terti perforatus et perforans - (See Plate 38)
6. M. flexor digitorum pedis profundus - (See Plate 40)
7. M. peroneus longus - (See Plate 37)

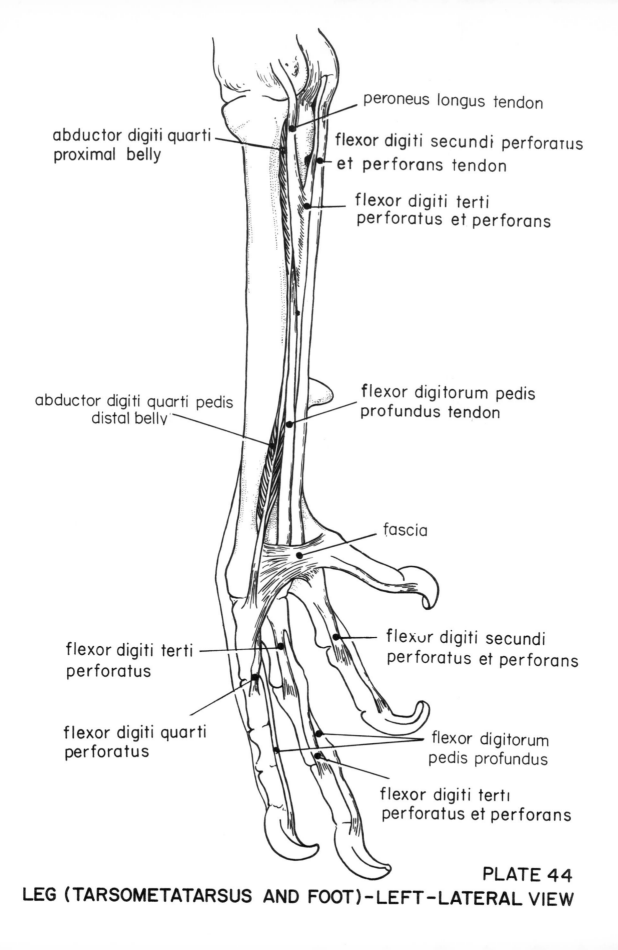

peroneus longus tendon

abductor digiti quarti
proximal belly

flexor digiti secundi perforatus
et perforans tendon

flexor digiti terti
perforatus et perforans

abductor digiti quarti pedis
distal belly

flexor digitorum pedis
profundus tendon

fascia

flexor digiti secundi
perforatus et perforans

flexor digiti terti
perforatus

flexor digitorum
pedis profundus

flexor digiti quarti
perforatus

flexor digiti terti
perforatus et perforans

PLATE 44

LEG (TARSOMETATARSUS AND FOOT)-LEFT-LATERAL VIEW

Plate 45   Leg (tarsometatarsus and foot) Left   Medial View

First Layer

1. M. abductor digiti secundi pedis - (See Plate 48)

2. M. adductor digiti secundi pedis, adductor of the second foot digit
     FORM AND RELATIONSHIPS: two bellies connected by a tendon; deep to
        tendons of flexor digitorum pedis profundus and superficial to plantar
        surface of tarsometatarsus.
     ORIGIN: hypotarsus, distal surface, by fibers.
     INSERTION: digit II phalanx I, proximolateral process, by a tendon.
     ACTION: adducts digit II.

3. M. extensor digiti terti pedis brevis - (See Plate 48)
4. M. extensor digitorum pedis longus - (See Plate 39)

5. M. extensor hallucis longus, long extensor of the great toe
     FORM AND RELATIONSHIPS: narrow, long; deep to tendons of extensor
        digitorum pedis longus, skin; superficial to dorsal surface of
        tarsometatarsus.
     ORIGIN: tarsometatarsus, proximal two-thirds medial surface, by fibers.
     INSERTION: fascia surrounding digit I, by a tendinous slip; and digit I
        the terminal phalanx, dorsal surface, by another tendinous slip.
     ACTION: extends and abducts hallux.

6. M. flexor digiti secundi perforatus et perforans - (See Plate 38)
7. M. flexor digiti terti perforatus et perforans - (See Plate 38)

8. M. flexor hallucis brevis, short flexor of the great toe
     FORM AND RELATIONSHIPS: triangular; deep to skin; superficial to
        plantar surface of tarsometatarsus.
     ORIGIN: tarsometatarsus, proximomedial surface, by fibers.
     INSERTION: digit I phalanx I, proximomedial surface by tendinous slip.
     ACTION: flexes and adducts hallux.

9. M. flexor hallucis longus - (See Plate 37)

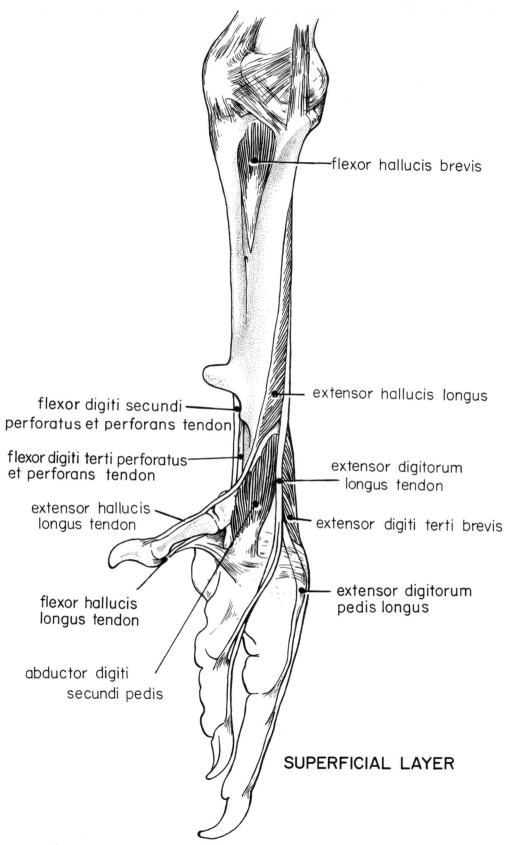

flexor hallucis brevis

extensor hallucis longus

flexor digiti secundi
perforatus et perforans tendon

flexor digiti terti perforatus
et perforans tendon

extensor digitorum
longus tendon

extensor hallucis
longus tendon

extensor digiti terti brevis

extensor digitorum
pedis longus

flexor hallucis
longus tendon

abductor digiti
secundi pedis

SUPERFICIAL LAYER

LEG (TARSOMETATARSUS AND FOOT) – LEFT – MEDIAL VIEW
PLATE 45

Plate 46   Leg (tarsometatarsus and foot) Left   Dorsal View

Superficial Layer
1. M. abductor digiti secundi pedis - (See Plate 48)
2. M. extensor digiti quarti pedis brevis - (See Plate 48)
3. M. extensor digiti terti pedis brevis - (See Plate 48)
4. M. extensor digitorum pedis longus - (See Plate 39)
5. M. extensor hallucis longus - (See Plate 45)
6. M. tibialis cranialis - (See Plate 38)

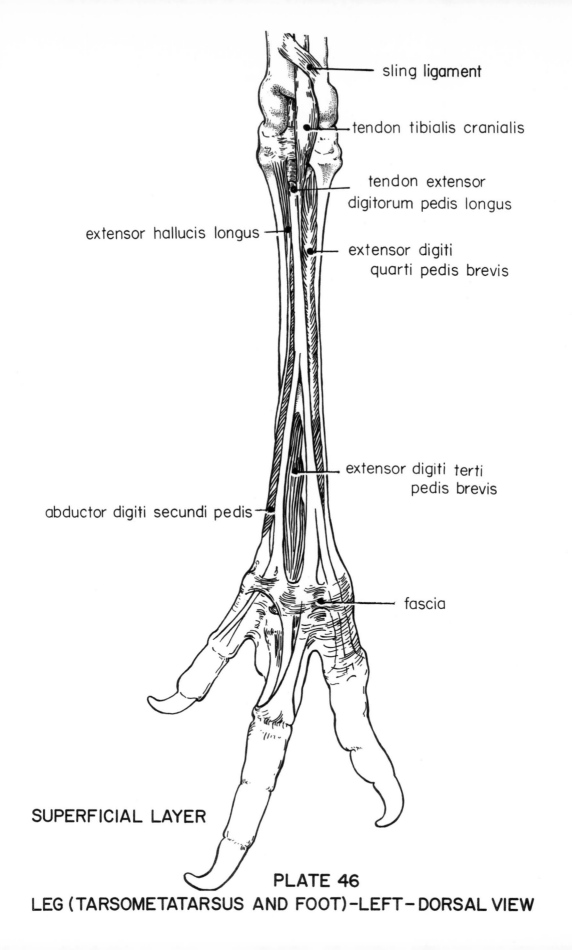

sling ligament

tendon tibialis cranialis

tendon extensor
digitorum pedis longus

extensor hallucis longus

extensor digiti
quarti pedis brevis

extensor digiti terti
pedis brevis

abductor digiti secundi pedis

fascia

SUPERFICIAL LAYER

PLATE 46
LEG (TARSOMETATARSUS AND FOOT)-LEFT-DORSAL VIEW

Plate 47   Foot   Left Dorsal View

Deep Layer
   1. M. extensor digitorum pedis longus - (See Plate 39)

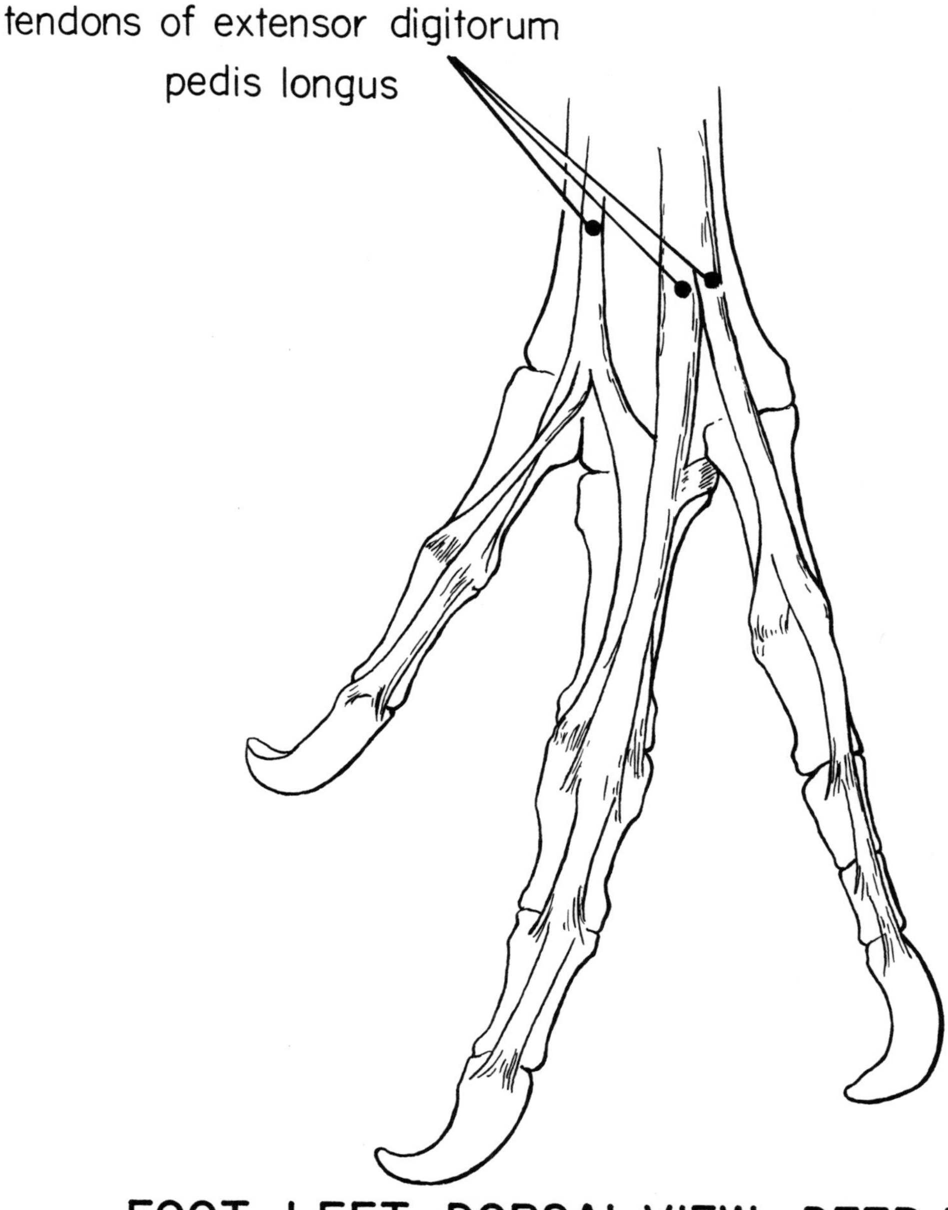

tendons of extensor digitorum
pedis longus

FOOT–LEFT–DORSAL VIEW DEEP LAYER
PLATE 47

Plate 48   Foot Left   Dorsal View

Deep Layer

1. M. abductor digiti secundi pedis, abductor of the second foot digit
   FORM AND RELATIONSHIPS: flat, short; deep to skin; superficial to
     metatarsal I, medial surface.
   ORIGIN: tarsometatarsus, distal-fifth medial surface, and metatarsal I,
     lateral surface, by fibers.
   INSERTION: digit II phalanx I, proximomedial process, by a tendon.
   ACTION: abducts digit II.

2. M. extensor digiti quarti pedis brevis, short extensor of the fourth digit
   FORM AND RELATIONSHIPS: thin, long; deep to tendons of extensor
     digitorum pedis longus; skin; superficial to dorsal surface of
     tarsometatarsus.
   ORIGIN: skin, fascia over tibiotarsus-tarsometatarsus articulation and
     tarsometatarsus, dorsal surface, by fibers.
   INSERTION: digit IV phalanx I, proximomedial process, by a tendon.
   ACTION: flexes and adducts digit IV.

3. M. extensor digiti terti pedis brevis, short extensor of the third digit
   FORM AND RELATIONSHIPS: triangular; small; deep to skin, tendons of
     extensor digitorum pedis longus; superficial to dorsodistal surface
     of the tarsometatarsus.
   ORIGIN: tarsometatarsus, dorsodistal one-fourth, by fibers.
   INSERTION: digit III phalanx I, proximodorsal articulating process, by
     a tendon.
   ACTION: flexes digit III.

4. M. extensor hallucis longus - (See Plate 45)
5. M. tibialis cranialis - (See Plate 38)

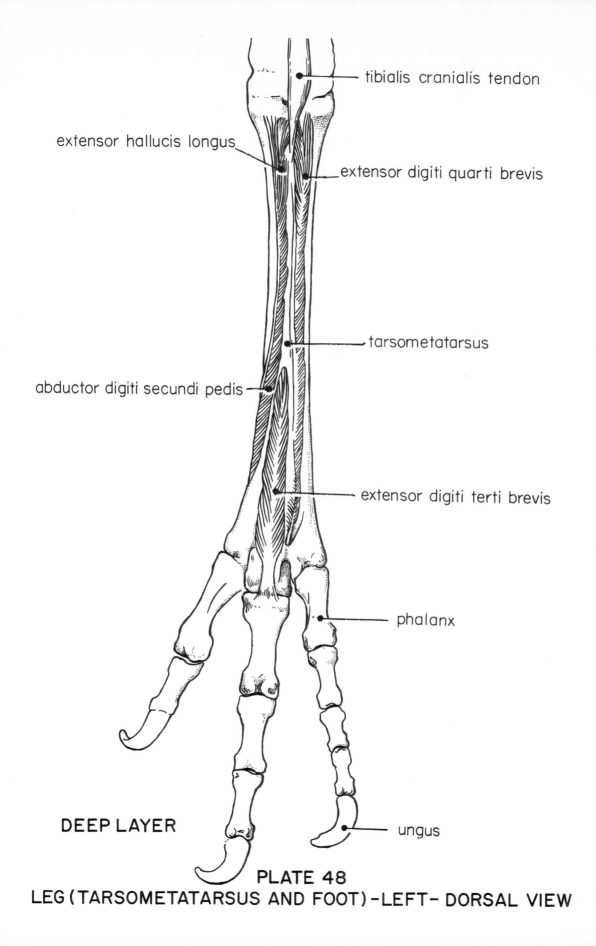

tibialis cranialis tendon

extensor hallucis longus

extensor digiti quarti brevis

tarsometatarsus

abductor digiti secundi pedis

extensor digiti terti brevis

phalanx

DEEP LAYER

ungus

PLATE 48
LEG (TARSOMETATARSUS AND FOOT) – LEFT – DORSAL VIEW

Plate 49   Tarsometatarsus and Foot   Dorsal View

Third Layer

1. M. abductor digiti secundi pedis - (See Plate 48)
2. M. adductor digiti secundi pedis - (See Plate 45)
3. M. extensor digitorum pedis longus - (See Plate 39)
4. M. flexor digiti quarti perforatus - (See Plate 42 - No. 6)
5. M. flexor digiti secundi perforatus - (See Plate 42 - No. 6)
6. M. flexor digiti secundi perforatus et perforans - (See Plate 38)
7. M. flexor digiti terti perforatus - (See Plate 42 - No. 6)
8. M. flexor digiti terti perforatus et perforans - (See Plate 38)
9. M. flexor digitorum pedis profundus - (See Plate 40)
10. M. flexor hallucis brevis - (See Plate 45)

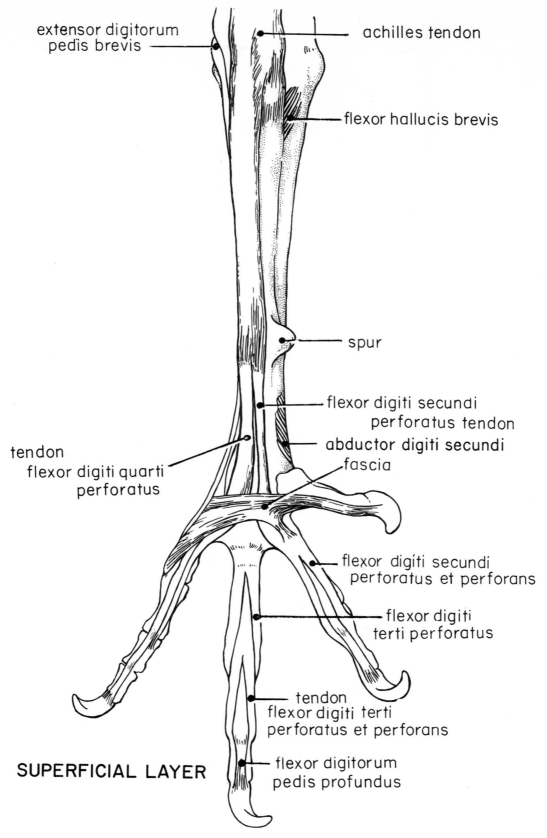

extensor digitorum
pedïs brevis

achilles tendon

flexor hallucis brevis

spur

flexor digiti secundi
perforatus tendon

abductor digiti secundi

fascia

tendon
flexor digiti quarti
perforatus

flexor digiti secundi
pertoratus et perforans

flexor digiti
terti perforatus

tendon
flexor digiti terti
perforatus et perforans

flexor digitorum
pedis profundus

SUPERFICIAL LAYER

LEG (TARSOMETATARSUS AND FOOT)-LEFT-PLANTAR VIEW
PLATE 49

Plate 50   Tarsometatarsus and Foot   Plantar View

Superficial Layer
1. M. abductor digiti secundi pedis - (See Plate 48)
2. M. adductor digiti quarti pedis - (See Plate 44)
3. M. flexor digiti quarti perforatus - (See Plate 42 - No. 6)
4. M. flexor digiti secundi perforatus et perforans - (See Plate 38)
5. M. flexor digiti terti perforatus - (See Plate 42 - No. 6)
6. M. flexor digiti terti perforatus et perforans - (See Plate 38)
7. M. flexor digitorum pedis profundus - (See Plate 40)
8. M. flexor digitorum pedis superficialis - (See Plate 42)
9. M. flexor hallucis brevis - (See Plate 45)

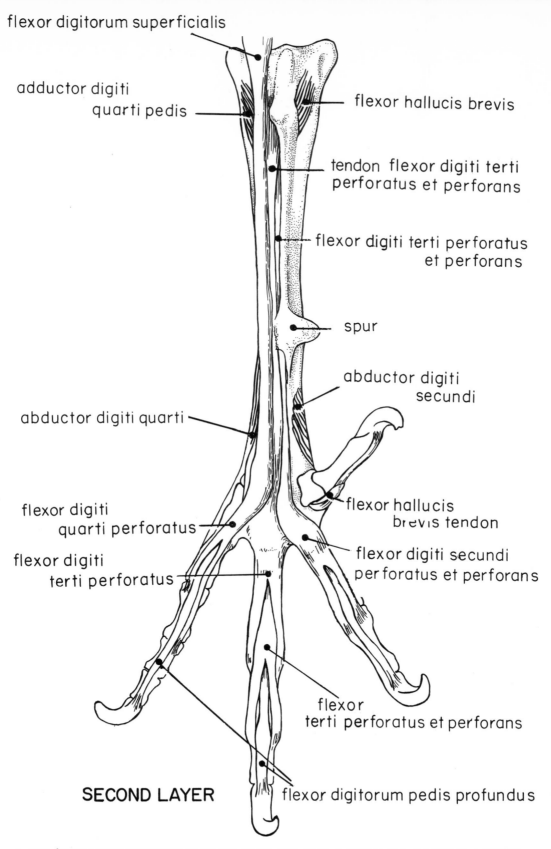

flexor digitorum superficialis

adductor digiti
quarti pedis

flexor hallucis brevis

tendon flexor digiti terti
perforatus et perforans

flexor digiti terti perforatus
et perforans

spur

abductor digiti
secundi

abductor digiti quarti

flexor digiti
quarti perforatus

flexor hallucis
brevis tendon

flexor digiti
terti perforatus

flexor digiti secundi
perforatus et perforans

flexor
terti perforatus et perforans

SECOND LAYER

flexor digitorum pedis profundus

LEG (TARSOMETATARSUS AND FOOT)-LEFT-PLANTAR VIEW
PLATE 50

Plate 51   Leg (tarsometatarsus and foot)   Plantar View

Second Layer
  1. M. abductor digiti quarti pedis - (See Plate 44)
  2. M. flexor digitorum pedis profundus - (See Plate 40)
  3. M. flexor hallucis brevis - (See Plate 45)
  4. M. flexor hallucis longus - (See Plate 37)

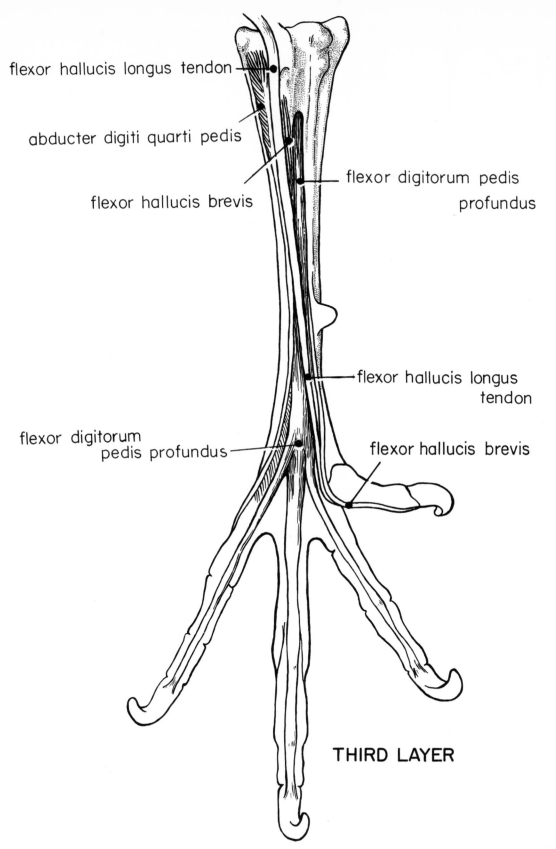

flexor hallucis longus tendon

abducter digiti quarti pedis

flexor hallucis brevis

flexor digitorum pedis profundus

flexor hallucis longus tendon

flexor digitorum pedis profundus

flexor hallucis brevis

THIRD LAYER

**LEG (TARSOMETATARSUS AND FOOT)-LEFT-PLANTAR VIEW
PLATE 51**

Plate 52   Tarsometatarsus and Foot   Plantar View

Fourth Layer (Deep)
  1. M. abductor digiti quarti pedis - (See Plate 44)
  2. M. abductor digiti secundi pedis - (See Plate 48)
  3. M. flexor hallucis brevis - (See Plate 45)

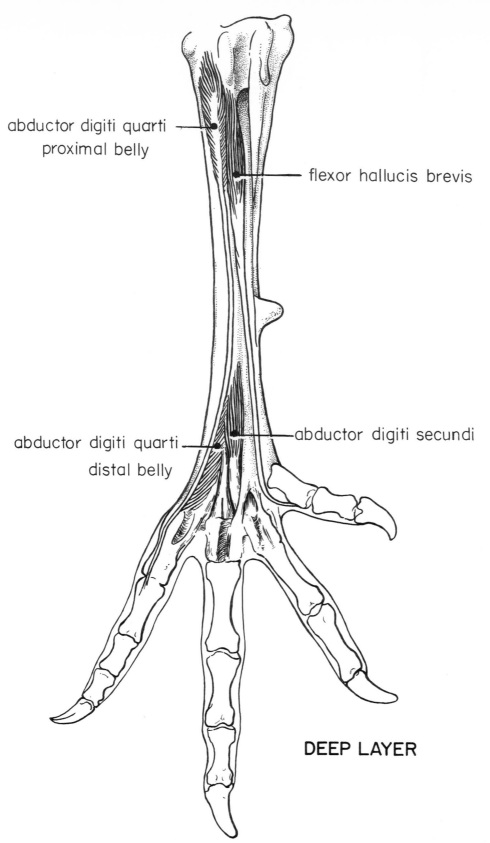

abductor digiti quarti
proximal belly

flexor hallucis brevis

abductor digiti quarti
distal belly

abductor digiti secundi

DEEP LAYER

LEG (TARSOMETATARSUS AND FOOT)-LEFT-PLANTAR VIEW
PLATE 52

Plate 53   Wing   Left Dorsal View

Superficial Layer
1. M. abductor digiti secundi manus - (See Plate 56)
2. M. adductor digiti secundi manus - (See Plate 56)
3. M. anconeus lateralis - (See Plate 54)
4. M. deltoideus - (See Plate 17)
5. M. extensor carpi radialis profundus - (See Plate 54)

6. M. extensor carpi radialis superficialis, the superficial extensor of the
   carpus
     FORM AND RELATIONSHIPS: long and fusiform; just under the skin; over
        the radius and extensor carpi radialis profundus; cranial to flexor
        digiti secundi et digiti terti manus and pronator brevis.
     ORIGIN: humerus, proximal to the external epicondylar prominence, by
        fibers and tendon.
     INSERTION: metacarpal II, distal process, by a tendon.
     ACTION: extends the carpometacarpus with assistance of the carpi
        radialis profundus.

7. M. extensor digiti secundi manus - (See Plate 55)

8. M. extensor digiti terti manus distalis, distal extensor of digit three
     FORM AND RELATIONSHIPS: broad and flat; lies ventrally on metacarpal
        III, just under the skin and tendons of extensor digiti terti manus
        medialis and flexor carpi ulnaris cranialis; ventral to adductor
        digiti secundi manus.
     ORIGIN: carpometacarpus, fusiform process, by fibers.
     INSERTION: digit III, phalanx II, by a tendon to proximoventral aspect
        of articular process; phalanx I of same digit by fascia to proximo-
        cranial aspect.
     ACTION: extends digit III.

9. M. extensor digiti terti manus lateralis - (See Plate 58)
10. M. flexor digiti secundi et digiti terti manus - (See Plate 55)

11. M. flexor metacarpi longus, long flexor of the metacarpus
     FORM AND RELATIONSHIPS: fusiform; most caudal of the superficial
        muscles of the forewing; deep to the skin and superficial to anconeus
        lateralis, supinator brevis and the ulna.
     ORIGIN: humerus, external epicondyle, by a tendon in common with that
        of the anconeus lateralis.
     INSERTION: metacarpal III, intermetacarpal process, caudal aspect and
        bases of the medial secondaries by a fascial connection from the
        tendon of origin.
     ACTION: flexes carpometacarpus with a slight abduction simultaneously,
        and elevates medial secondaries.

12. M. interosseus dorsalis, dorsal interosseus muscle
     FORM AND RELATIONSHIPS: small and flat; between metacarpals III and V,
        deep to the skin and superficial to interosseus ventralis.
     ORIGIN: metacarpals III and V, by fibers.
     INSERTION: digit III, phalanx I, by a tendon.
     ACTION: supinates digit III.

13. M. latissimus dorsi - (See Plate 16)
14. M. patagialis - (See Plate 20)
15. M. pectoralis superficialis - (See Plate 20)

16. M. tensor patagii longus - (See Plate 20)
17. M. triceps caput dorsale - (See Plate 17)

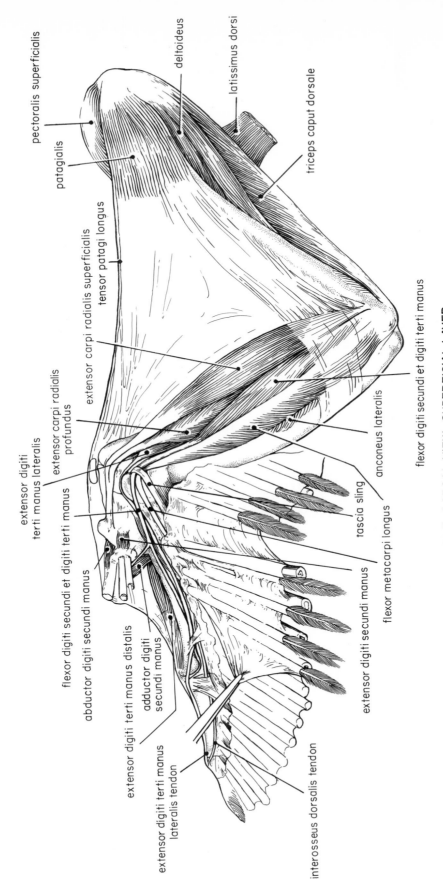

pectoralis superficialis

patagialis

deltoideus

latissimus dorsi

triceps caput dorsale

extensor carpi radialis superficialis
tensor patagi longus

extensor carpi radialis
profundus

flexor digiti secundi et digiti terti manus

flexor digiti secundi et digiti terti manus

anconeus lateralis

extensor digiti
terti manus lateralis

fascia sling

flexor metacarpi longus

flexor digiti secundi et digiti terti manus

abductor digiti secundi manus

extensor digiti terti manus distalis

adductor digiti
secundi manus

extensor digiti secundi manus

extensor digiti terti manus
lateralis tendon

interosseus dorsalis tendon

WING–LEFT–DORSAL VIEW SUPERFICIAL LAYER
PLATE 53

Plate 54   Wing   Left Dorsal View

Second Layer
  1. M. abductor digiti secundi manus - (See Plate 56)
  2. M. adductor digiti secundi manus - (See Plate 56)

  3. M. anconeus lateralis, lateral anconeus muscle
       FORM AND RELATIONSHIPS: fusiform; broad; deep to flexor metacarpi
         longus and flexor digiti secundi et digiti terti manus and
         superficial to humerus and ulna concave surface.
       ORIGIN: humerus external epicondyle, by a tendon in common with that
         of the flexor metacarpi longus.
       INSERTION: ulna, intermuscular line, by fibers.
       ACTION: flexes antibrachium.

  4. M. biceps brachii, biceps muscle of the brachium
       FORM AND RELATIONSHIPS: long, fusiform; two fasciculi; just under skin
         on lateral surface of humerus.
       ORIGIN: coracoid, brachial tuberosity, by a broad flat tendon.
       INSERTION: (a) ulna, bicipital prominence, by a tendon which passes
         superficially over inserting tendon of ventral fasciculus.
                   (b) radius, just distal to head radius, by two small tendons.
       ACTION: flexes antibrachium.

  5. M. brachialis - (See Plate 58)
  6. M. deltoideus - (See Plate 17)

  7. M. extensor carpi radialis profundus, deep extensor of the carpus
       FORM AND RELATIONSHIPS: fusiform; just under the skin and flexor
         digiti secundi et digiti terti manus and overlies (medially) the
         radius, extensor carpi obliquus, extensor digiti terti manus medialis,
         pronator longus and brachialis.
       ORIGIN: radius and ulna proximal articulation and concave borders, by
         fibers.
       INSERTION: metacarpal II, distal process, by a tendon in common with
         that of the extensor carpi radialis superficialis.
       ACTION: extends carpometacarpus with assistance of extensor carpi
         radialis superficialis.

  8. M. extensor carpi radialis superficialis - (See Plate 53)
  9. M. extensor digiti secundi manus - (See Plate 55)
 10. M. extensor digiti terti manus distalis - (See Plate 53)
 11. M. extensor digiti terti manus lateralis - (See Plate 58)
 12. M. flexor digiti secundi et digiti terti manus - (See Plate 55)
 13. M. flexor metacarpi caudalis - (See Plate 55)
 14. M. flexor metacarpi longus - (See Plate 53)
 15. M. interosseus dorsalis - (See Plate 53)
 16. M. interosseus ventralis - (See Plate 55)
 17. M. latissimus dorsi - (See Plate 16)
 18. M. patagialis - (See Plate 20)
 19. M. pectoralis profundus - (See Plate 21)
 20. M. pectoralis superficialis - (See Plate 20)
 21. M. scapulohumeralis maximus - (See Plate 18)

 22. M. supinator brevis, short supinator
       FORM AND RELATIONSHIPS: bandlike; most cranial of the second layer
         of muscles of the forewing; deep to extensor carpi radialis
         superficialis, flexor metacarpi longus, flexor digiti secundi et

digiti <u>terti</u> <u>manus</u>, and tendon of <u>anconeus</u> <u>lateralis</u>; superficial to the radius and <u>pronator</u> <u>brevis</u>.

ORIGIN: humerus, external epicondyle by a tendon.

INSERTION: radius, proximal third, by fibers.

ACTION: supinates and flexes the antibrachium.

23. <u>M</u>. <u>tensor</u> <u>patagii</u> <u>longus</u> - (See Plate 20)
24. <u>M</u>. <u>triceps</u> <u>caput</u> <u>dorsale</u> - (See Plate 17)
25. <u>M</u>. <u>triceps</u> <u>caput</u> <u>internale</u> - (See Plate 18)

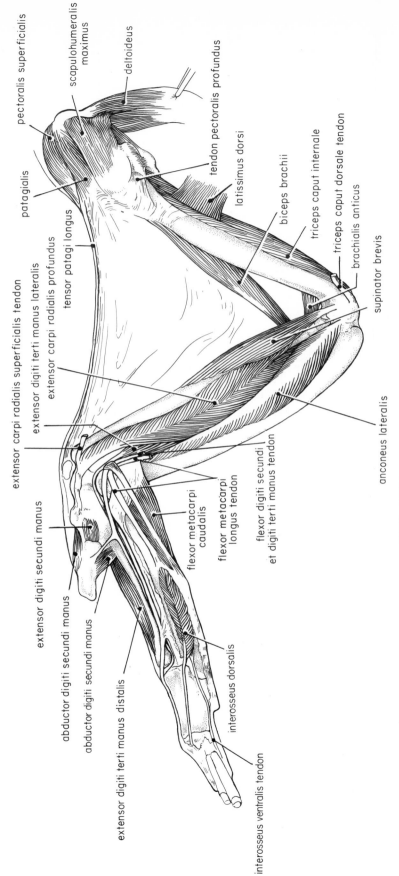

pectoralis superficialis

scapulohumeralis maximus

deltoideus

tendon pectoralis profundus

latissimus dorsi

biceps brachii

triceps caput internale

triceps caput dorsale tendon

brachialis anticus

supinator brevis

patagialis

extensor carpi radialis superficialis tendon

extensor digiti terti manus lateralis

extensor carpi radialis profundus

tensor patagi longus

extensor digiti secundi manus

abductor digiti secundi manus

abductor digiti secundi manus

extensor digiti terti manus distalis

interosseus dorsalis

flexor metacarpi caudalis

flexor metacarpi longus tendon

flexor digiti secundi et digiti terti manus tendon

anconeus lateralis

interosseus ventralis tendon

WING–LEFT–DORSAL VIEW SECOND LAYER
PLATE 54

Plate 55   Wing Left   Dorsal View

Third Layer
1. M. abductor digiti secundi manus - (See Plate 56)
2. M. adductor digiti secundi manus - (See Plate 56)
3. M. extensor carpi obliquus - (See Plate 58)
4. M. extensor carpi radialis profundus - (See Plate 54)
5. M. extensor carpi radialis superficialis - (See Plate 53)

6. M. extensor digiti secundi manus, extensor of the second wing digit
    FORM AND RELATIONSHIPS: small and triangular; deep to the skin and
        superficial to the adductor digiti secundi manus and metacarpal II.
    ORIGIN: metacarpal II, dorsal aspect, by fibers.
    INSERTION: phalanx of digit II, cranioproximal articular process, by a
        tendon.
    ACTION: extends and suppinates digit II.

7. M. extensor digiti terti manus distalis - (See Plate 53)
8. M. extensor digiti terti manus lateralis - (See Plate 58)
9. M. extensor digiti terti manus medialis - (See Plate 56)
10. M. flexor digiti quarti manus longus - (See Plate 57)

11. M. flexor digiti secundi et digiti terti manus, the flexor of the second
    and third digits of the wing
    FORM AND RELATIONSHIPS: delicate and fusiform terminating in one long
        and one short tendon; just under the skin; caudal to extensor carpi
        radialis superficialis; cranial to flexor metacarpi longus; over
        anconeus lateralis, extensor carpi radialis profundus and supinator
        brevis.
    ORIGIN: humerus, external epicondylar prominence, by a tendon.
    INSERTION: digit II, by the short tendon to the caudal aspect of the
        phalanx; digit III, by the long tendon to the proximoventral process
        of the first phalanx.
    ACTION: supinates digit II; but extends digit III; flexes
        carpometacarpus.

12. M. flexor digiti secundi manus, flexor of the second wing digit -
    (See Plate 56)

13. M. flexor et abductor digiti quarti manus, the flexor and abductor of the
    fourth digit of the wing
    FORM AND RELATIONSHIPS: small and fusiform; just under the skin; on
        distal part of metacarpal IV dorsally and caudally.
    ORIGIN: metacarpal IV, from the distal tenth dorsocaudally, by fibers.
    INSERTION: digit IV, phalanx I, proximocaudal articular process, by a
        tendon.
    ACTION: flexes and abducts digit IV.

14. M. flexor metacarpi brevis, short flexor of the metacarpals
    FORM AND RELATIONSHIPS: small and delicate; deep to the skin and
        overlying the adductor digiti secundi manus, flexor digiti secundi
        manus, and metacarpal III.
    ORIGIN: radial carpal, dorsodistal angle, by fibers.
    INSERTION: metacarpal III cranial aspect, by fibers, and to the
        tendinous slip of flexor digiti secundi et digiti manus which in
        turn inserts on the articular process of phalanx I of digit III.
    ACTION: aids in extending and supinating digit III; it may also aid
        in flexing the carpometacarpus.

138

15. **M. flexor metacarpi caudalis**, caudal flexor of the metacarpus

    FORM AND RELATIONSHIPS: narrowly wedge shaped; composed of three fasciculi; deep to the skin and inserting tendons of flexor digiti quarti manus longus and flexor metacarpi longus; superficial to the ulna.

    ORIGIN: ulna dorsocranial aspect, by a tendon common to the dorsal and ventral fasciculi; and ulnar carpal, by a tendon from the intermediate fasciculus.

    INSERTION: metacarpal IV, by the dorsal and intermediate fasciculus and to follicles of the primary feathers by fascia from the ventral fasciculus.

    ACTION: flexes the metacarpus and spreads the primaries.

16. **M. flexor metacarpi longus** - (See Plate 53)
17. **M. interosseus dorsalis** - (See Plate 53)

18. **M. interosseus ventralis**, ventral interosseus muscle

    FORM AND RELATIONSHIPS: small; deep to the skin and ventral (deep) to interosseus dorsalis; lies between metacarpals III and IV.

    ORIGIN: metacarpals III and IV internal surfaces, by fibers.

    INSERTION: digit III, phalanx II, ventral surface, by a tendon.

    ACTION: supinates digit III and flexes phalanx II.

19. **M. latissimus dorsi** - (See Plate 16)
20. **M. supinator brevis** - (See Plate 54)

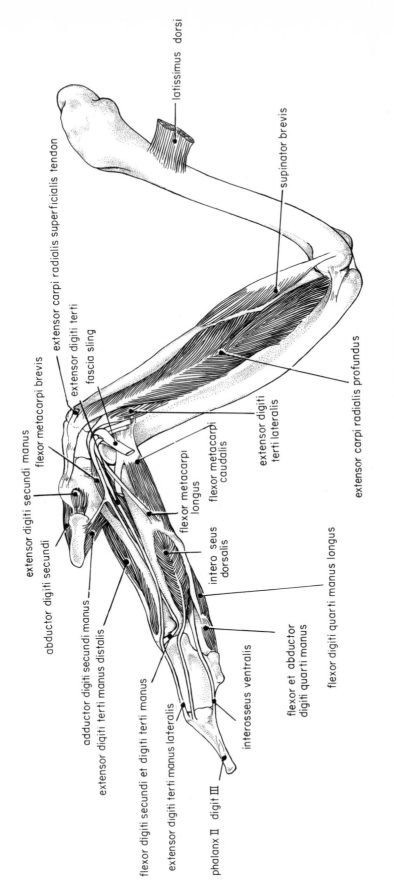

latissimus dorsi

supinator brevis

extensor carpi radialis superficialis tendon

extensor digiti terti

fascia sling

flexor metacarpi brevis

extensor digiti secundi manus

extensor carpi radialis profundus

extensor digiti terti lateralis

flexor metacarpi caudalis

flexor metacarpi longus

abductor digiti secundi

adductor digiti secundi manus

extensor digiti terti manus distalis

intero seus dorsalis

flexor digiti secundi et digiti terti manus

extensor digiti terti manus lateralis

flexor digiti quarti manus longus

phalanx II   digit III

interosseus ventralis

flexor et abductor digiti quarti manus

WING – LEFT – DORSAL VIEW THIRD LAYER
PLATE 55

Plate 56   Wing Left   Ventral View

Superficial Layer

1. M. abductor digiti secundi manus, abductor of the second wing digit
     FORM AND RELATIONSHIPS: triangular along the cranial and ventral
        surfaces of the phalanx of digit II.
     ORIGIN: tendinous slip from the tensor patagii longus near insertion
        of the latter.
     INSERTION: phalanx I of digit II cranial and ventral surface, by fibers.
     ACTION: abducts digit II.

2. M. adductor digiti secundi manus, adductor of the second wing digit
     FORM AND RELATIONSHIPS: thin and delicate; in the caudal aspect of
        digit II; deep to the skin and flexor metacarpi brevis and overlying
        extensor digiti terti manus distalis.
     ORIGIN: metacarpal III proximocranial aspect.
     INSERTION: digit II, phalanx I, caudal aspect.
     ACTION: adducts digit II.

3. M. biceps brachii - (See Plate 54)
4. M. brachialis - (See Plate 58)
5. M. extensor carpi obliquus - (See Plate 58)
6. M. extensor carpi radialis profundus - (See Plate 54)
7. M. extensor carpi radialis superficialis - (See Plate 53)
8. M. extensor digiti terti manus distalis - (See Plate 53)

9. M. extensor digiti terti manus medialis
     FORM AND RELATIONSHIPS: fusiform with extensive tendon extending
        distally from the wrist joint; under brachialis, anconeus medialis,
        flexor carpi ulnaris cranialis and flexor carpi ulnaris caudalis;
        over extensor carpi obliquus and ulna.
     ORIGIN: ulna, proximal half of the radial face, by fibers.
     INSERTION: digit III, phalanx II, proximocranial angle, by a tendon.
     ACTION: extends digit III and carpometacarpus.

10. M. flexor carpi ulnaris caudalis, caudal ulnar flexor of the carpus
     FORM AND RELATIONSHIPS: the most caudal of the radio-ulnar group;
        fusiform; along the caudal border of the ulna; under fascia of flexor
        carpi ulnaris cranialis and skin.
     ORIGIN: humerus, external epicondyle medial surface, by a tendon.
     INSERTION: ulnar carpal, medial surface, by a strong tendon.
     ACTION: flexes carpometacarpus.

11. M. flexor carpi ulnaris cranialis, the cranial ulnar flexor of the carpus
     FORM AND RELATIONSHIPS: this is principally a tendinous fascia over
        the flexor carpi ulnaris caudalis.
     ORIGIN: humerus, internal epicondylar prominence, by a tough tendon.
     INSERTION: the inserting tendon passes ventral to ulnar carpal and
        continues distally along metacarpal III. At the articulation of
        metacarpal III and phalanx I of digit III it divides into two small
        muscular slips which insert on the proximodorsal aspect of phalanx II;
        fascia from this inserting area extends proximally to insert at the
        bases of the caudal feather follicles of the wing.
     ACTION: extends digit III and flexes the carpus slightly.

12. M. flexor digiti quarti manus longus - (See Plate 57)

13. M. flexor digiti secundi manus, flexor of the second hand digit
    FORM AND RELATIONSHIPS: straplike; short and delicate; deep to the skin
        and adductor digiti secundi manus, caudal to metacarpal II and
        superficial to the flexor metacarpi brevis.
    ORIGIN: carpus cranial fossa, by fibers.
    INSERTION: digit II, phalanx I, caudoventral articular process, by
        fibers.
    ACTION: flexes digit II.

14. M. interosseus ventralis - (See Plate 55)
15. M. latissimus dorsi - (See Plate 16)
16. M. patagialis - (See Plate 20)

17. M. pronator brevis, short pronator of the wing
    FORM AND RELATIONSHIPS: fusiform; just under skin; cranial to
        pronator longus and extensor digiti terti manus medialis; over biceps
        brachii insertion, supinator brevis, brachialis anticus, and radius.
    ORIGIN: humerus, internal epicondylar tuberosity, by a tendon, just
        proximal to origin of pronator longus.
    INSERTION: radius, mid-lateral surface, by fibers.
    ACTION: acts with the pronator longus to pronate antibrachium.

18. M. pronator longus, long pronator of the wing
    FORM AND RELATIONSHIPS: fusiform; just under skin; cranial to flexor
        carpi ulnaris cranialis and anconeus medialis; caudal to pronator
        brevis; over insertion of biceps brachii and ventral surface of radius.
    ORIGIN: humerus, internal epicondylar prominence, by a tendon in
        common with that of anconeus medialis.
    INSERTION: radius, ventral surface of shaft, by fibers.
    ACTION: acts in common with the pronator brevis to pronate antibrachium.

19. M. tensor patagii caudalis - (See Plate 20)
20. M. tensor patagii longus - (See Plate 20)
21. M. teres - (See Plate 17)
22. M. triceps caput dorsale - (See Plate 17)
23. M. triceps caput internale - (See Plate 18)
24. M. triceps caput ventrale - (See Plate 18)

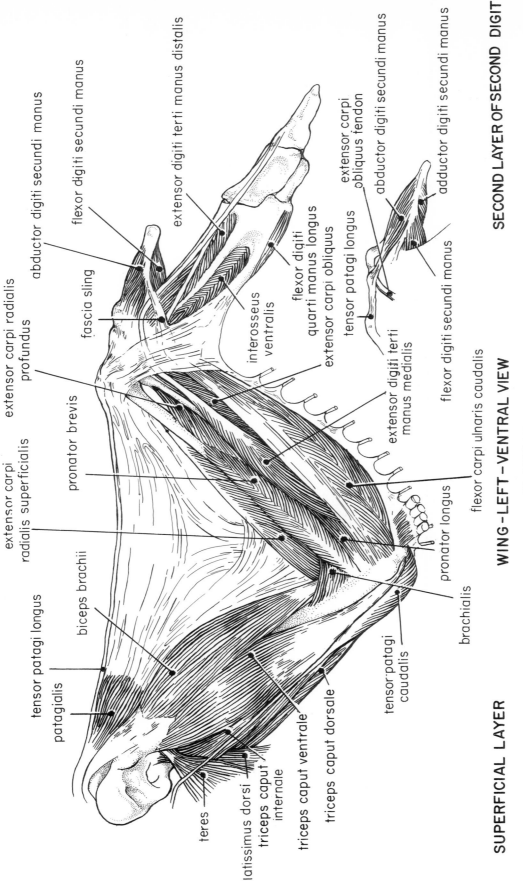

tensor patagi longus

patagialis

extensor carpi
radialis superficialis

biceps brachii

pronator brevis

teres

latissimus dorsi

triceps caput
internale

triceps caput ventrale

triceps caput dorsale

tensor patagi
caudalis

brachialis

extensor carpi radialis
profundus

abductor digiti secundi manus

fascia sling

flexor digiti secundi manus

abductor digiti secundi manus

extensor digiti terti manus distalis

interosseus
ventralis

flexor digiti
quarti manus longus

extensor carpi obliquus

tensor patagi longus

extensor digiti terti
manus medialis

flexor digiti secundi manus

flexor carpi ulnaris caudalis

pronator longus

extensor carpi
obliquus tendon

abductor digiti secundi manus

adductor digiti secundi manus

flexor digiti secundi manus

SUPERFICIAL LAYER

SECOND LAYER OF SECOND DIGIT

WING—LEFT—VENTRAL VIEW

PLATE 56

Plate 57   Wing Left   Ventral View

Second Layer

1. M. anconeus medialis, medial elbow muscle
    FORM AND RELATIONSHIPS: flat, triangular; under flexor carpi ulnaris
       caudalis and flexor carpi ulnaris cranialis; caudal to pronator longus;
       over brachialis and extensor digiti terti manus medialis, ulna and
       humero-ulnar articulation.
    ORIGIN: humerus, internal epicondylar prominence in common with that of
       pronator brevis by a tendon.
    INSERTION: ulna, proximal third of ventral surface by fibers.
    ACTION: extends antibrachium.

2. M. biceps brachii - (See Plate 54)
3. M. brachialis - (See Plate 58)
4. M. extensor carpi obliquus - (See Plate 58)
5. M. extensor carpi radialis profundus - (See Plate 54)
6. M. extensor carpi radialis superficialis - (See Plate 53)
7. M. extensor digiti terti manus distalis - (See Plate 53)
8. M. extensor digiti terti manus lateralis - (See Plate 58)
9. M. extensor digiti terti manus medialis - (See Plate 56)
10. M. flexor carpi ulnaris caudalis - (See Plate 56)

11. M. flexor digiti quarti manus longus
    FORM AND RELATIONSHIPS: long narrow band, deep to the skin and caudal
       to metacarpal IV; superficial to flexor metacarpi caudalis.
    ORIGIN: ulnar carpal and metacarpal IV, by fibers.
    INSERTION: digit IV phalanx I, proximocaudal articular process by a
       tendon in common with that of the flexor et abductor digiti quarti
       manus.
    ACTION: flexes digit IV.

12. M. flexor digiti secundi manus - (See Plate 56)
13. M. flexor metacarpi caudalis - (See Plate 55)
14. M. interosseus dorsalis - (See Plate 53)
15. M. latissimus dorsi - (See Plate 16)
16. M. patagialis - (See Plate 20)
17. M. pronator brevis - (See Plate 56)
18. M. supinator brevis - (See Plate 54)
19. M. triceps caput dorsale - (See Plate 17)
20. M. triceps caput internale - (See Plate 18)
21. M. triceps caput ventrale - (See Plate 18)

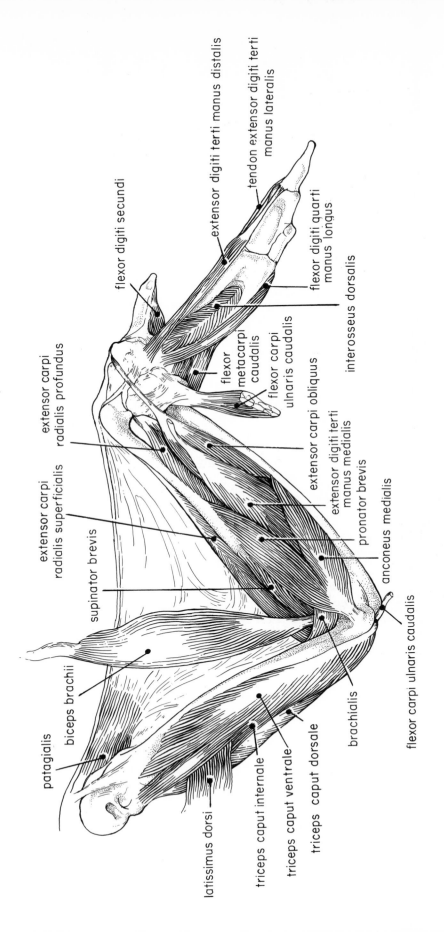

extensor digiti terti manus distalis

tendon extensor digiti terti manus lateralis

extensor digiti terti manus distalis

flexor digiti secundi

flexor digiti quarti manus longus

interosseus dorsalis

flexor metacarpi caudalis

flexor carpi ulnaris caudalis

extensor carpi radialis profundus

extensor carpi obliquus

extensor digiti terti manus medialis

pronator brevis

anconeus medialis

extensor carpi radialis superficialis

supinator brevis

flexor carpi ulnaris caudalis

patagialis

biceps brachii

latissimus dorsi

triceps caput internale

triceps caput ventrale

triceps caput dorsale

brachialis

WING–LEFT–VENTRAL VIEW SECOND LAYER
PLATE 57

Plate 58   Wing Left   Ventral View

Deep Layer
1. M. anconeus lateralis - (See Plate 54)

2. M. brachialis
    FORM AND RELATIONSHIPS: short, straplike at humero-ulnar articulation;
        ventral to pronator brevis, pronator longus and anconeus medialis;
        cranial to cubital ligament; over extensor digiti terti manus medialis
        and inserting tendon of biceps brachii.
    ORIGIN: humerus, brachialis depression by fibers.
    INSERTION: ulna, brachialis depression by fibers.
    ACTION: flexes antibrachium upon brachium.

3. M. extensor carpi obliquus, oblique extensor of the carpus
    FORM AND RELATIONSHIPS: broad and flat; on distal third of ulna
        ventrally; under extensor digiti terti manus medialis, and flexor carpi
        ulnaris caudalis.
    ORIGIN: ulna, distal third ventrally by fibers.
    INSERTION: carpometacarpus II, proximal protuberance dorsally by a
        tendon which passes obliquely over radial carpal.
    ACTION: extends and pronates the manus.

4. M. extensor carpi obliquus - (See Plate 58)

5. M. extensor digiti terti manus lateralis
    FORM AND RELATIONSHIPS: thin and fusiform; under the pronator brevis
        and the skin; over the extensor carpi radialis profundus and the
        concavity of the radius distally.
    ORIGIN: radius, distal half of the concave surface by fibers.
    INSERTION: digit III, phalanx I, by a tendon. This tendon passes over
        the articulation of ulna and carpometacarpus laterally and then to
        dorsal surface of metacarpal III before inserting on the phalanx. Near
        the articulation of ulna and carpometacarpus it receives an incon-
        spicuous muscular slip from the aponeurosis which covers the dorsal
        surface of the manus.
    ACTION: extends digit III and aids in extension of whole manus.

6. M. extensor digiti terti manus medialis - (See Plate 56)
7. M. supinator brevis - (See Plate 54)

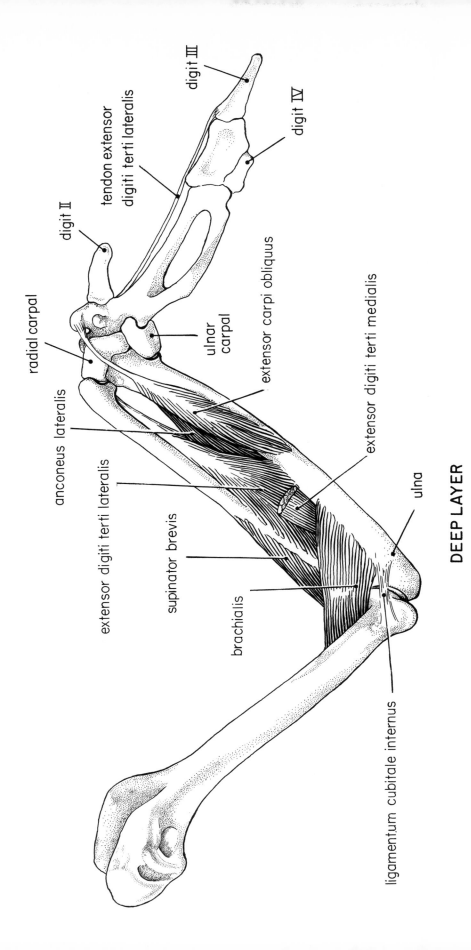

digit III

tendon extensor
digiti terti lateralis

digit IV

digit II

radial carpal

ulnar
carpal

extensor carpi obliquus

anconeus lateralis

extensor digiti terti medialis

extensor digiti terti lateralis

supinator brevis

ulna

brachialis

ligamentum cubitale internus

DEEP LAYER

**WING–LEFT–VENTRAL VIEW
PLATE 58**

Table I - Bird Muscle Synonomies*

Harvey, Kaiser Rosenberg (Turkey)	George + Berger (Aves)	Romer (Aves)	Fisher (Whooping Crane)	Howell (Aves)	Chamberlain (Chicken)	Shufeldt (Raven)
abductor digiti quarti pedis	abductor digiti IV		abductor digiti IV		interossei	
abductor digiti secundi pedis	abductor digiti II		abductor digiti II			
abductor digiti secundi manus	abductor pollicis		abductor pollicis			extensor proprius pollicis
adductor digiti secundi manus	adductor pollicis		adductor pollicis	adductor pollicis	adductor of the second digit	flexor brevis pollicis
adductor digiti secundi pedis	adductor digiti II		adductor digiti II			
adductor longus	adductor longus	puboischio-femoralis	adductor super-ficialis	adductor super-ficialis	adductor 1. lateral 2. medial	adductor longus
adductor magnus	adductor profundus		adductor profundus	adductor profundus		adductor magnus
ambiens	ambiens	ambiens	ambiens	ambiens	pectineus	ambiens
anconeus lateralis	anconeus	extensor antebrachii ulnaris	anconeus		anconeus	anconeus
anconeus medialis					anconeus medialis	

articulohyoideus	stylo-hyoideus				articulo-hyoideus	stylo-hyoideus
articulomylo-hyoideus	platysma myoides				cutaneous aucheniatria	platysma myoides
basientoglossus					copuloento-glossum	
basirectricales	lateralis caudae		lateralis caudae			lateralis caudae
biceps brachii	biceps brachii	biceps brachii	biceps	biceps	biceps brachii	biceps
biceps flexor cruris	biceps flexor cruris	iliofibu-laris	extensor ilio-fibularis	extensor ilio-fibularis	biceps flexor cruris	biceps flexor cruris
biventer cervicis	biventer cervicis				biventer cervicis	biventer cervicis
biventer maxillae	depressor mandibulae				occipito-mandibularis	biventer maxillae
brachialis	brachialis	brachialis	brachialis	brachialis	brachialis	brachialis
caudalis lateralis	lateralis coccygis	lateralis coccygis	lateralis coccygis		lateralis coccygeus	lateralis coccygis
ceratoentoglossus	cerato-hyoideus				styloento-glossum	cerato-hyoideus
circumconcha (Not figured)	circum-concha					circum-concha
complexus	complexus			complexus	complexus	complexus

Table I - Bird Muscle Synonomies (continued)

Harvey, Kaiser, Rosenberg	George + Berger	Romer	Fisher	Howell	Chamberlain	Shufeldt
coracobrachialis dorsalis	coraco-brachialis anterior		coracobra-chialis anterior subcor-accoideus	coracobra-chialis anterior subcor-accoideus	supracora-coid	coraco-brachialis
coracobrachialis ventralis	coraco-brachialis posterior	coracobra-chialis	coracobra-chialis posterior	coracobra-chialis posterior	coracobra-chialis ventralis	pectoralis tertius
coracohumeralis	coraco-humeralis		coracobra-chialis anterior	coracobra-chialis anterior		coraco-humeralis
cutaneus cleido-dorsalis	dermocleido-dorsalis				cutaneus cleido-dorsalis	dermocleido-dorsalis
cutaneus colli lateralis	cutaneus colli				cutaneus colli lateralis	dermo-temporalis
cutaneus costohumeralis	dermo-ulnaris				cutaneus costo-humeralis	dermo-ulnaris
cutaneus iliacus	dermo-iliacus				cutaneus iliacus	dermo-iliacus

cutaneus nuchalis	cleido- trachealis		cutaneus nuchalis	cleido- trachealis
cutaneus pectoralis caudalis	dermo- pectoralis		cutaneus trunci- ventralis	dermo- pectoralis
cutaneus pectoralis cranialis	dermo- pectoralis		cutaneus cleido- ventralis	dermo- pectoralis
cutaneus spinalis dorsalis	dermo- spinalis		cutaneus spina- lis dorsalis	dermo- spinalis
deltoideus	deltoideus	deltoideus minor	deltoideus	scapulo- humeralis
				deltoideus deep-brevis
depressor caudae	depressor caudae	depressor coccygis	depressor coccygis	depressor coccygis
depressor glossi	depressor glossus			depressor glossus
depressor palpebrarum ventralis	depressor palpebrae inferio- ris		depressor palpebrarum ventralis	depressor palpebrarum interior
depressor rectricum	depressor caudae	depressor caudae	coccygeus	depressor caudae
diaphragma	costopulmonares			diaphragma
entotympanicus			pterygo- palatinus	ento- tympanicus
eversor urodeum	levator cloacae	levator cloacae	eversor urodeum	

Table I - Bird Muscle Synonomies (continued)

Harvey, Kaiser, Rosenberg	George + Berger	Romer	Fisher	Howell	Chamberlain	Shufeldt
extensor carpi obliquus	flexor carpi ulnaris brevis		flexor carpi ulnaris		extensor carpi obliquus	flexor carpi ulnaris brevior
extensor carpi radialis profundus	extensor metacarpi radialis		extensor metacarpi radialis pars palmaris		extensor carpi radialis; deep head	
extensor carpi radialis superficialis	extensor metacarpi radialis		extensor metacarpi radialis pars anconalis		extensor carpi radialis	extensor meta-carpi radialis longior
extensor digiti quarti pedis brevis	extensor brevis digiti IV		extensor brevis digiti IV			
extensor digiti secundi manus	extensor pollicis brevis		extensor pollicis brevis		extensor digiti secundi	
extensor digiti terti manus distalis	abductor indicis		abductor indicis			
extensor digiti terti manus lateralis	extensor indicis longus		extensor indicis longus		extensor digiti terti	extensor indicis longus
extensor digiti terti manus medialis	flexor digitorum profundus		flexor digitorum profundus		extensor digiti terti	flexor digitorum profundus

extensor digiti terti pedis brevis	extensor brevis digiti III			extensor brevis digiti III
extensor digitorum pedis longus	extensor digitorum communis	extensor digitorum longus	extensor longus digitorum	extensor digitus longus digitorum
extensor femoris	extensor femoris		rectus femoris	
crureus	vastus medialis	vastus medialis	medial vasti	crureus
subcrureus				
vastus externus	vastus externus	vastus lateralis	lateral vasti	vastus externus
vastus internus	vastus internus	femori-tibialis internus		vastus internus
extensor hallucis longus	extensor hallucis longus	extensor hallucis longus	extensor hallucis brevis	extensor hallucis brevis
obliquus abdominis externus	obliquus abdominis externus	obliquus abdominis externus	obliquus abdominis externus	obliquus externus abdominis
flexor carpi ulnaris caudalis	flexor carpi ulnaris	flexor carpi ulnaris, posterior part	flexor carpi ulnaris	flexor carpi ulnaris
flexor carpi ulnaris cranialis		flexor carpi ulnaris, anterior part		

Table I - Bird Muscle Synonomies (continued)

Harvey, Kaiser, Rosenberg	George + Berger	Romer	Fisher	Howell	Chamberlain	Shufeldt
flexor digiti quarti manus longus	flexor digiti IV		flexor digiti III		flexor longus digiti quarti	flexor minimi digiti
flexor digiti secundi manus	flexor digiti II		adductor pollicis		adductor of the second digit	flexor brevis pollicis
flexor digiti secundi et digiti terti manus	extensor digitorum communis		extensor digitorum communis			extensor digitorum communis
flexor digiti secundi per-foratus et perforans	flexor per-forans and perforatus digiti II		flexor per-forans et perforatus digiti II		flexor digitus perforatus et perforans digiti secun-di (median digital interme-diate flexor)	flexor perfo-ratus indicis secundus pedis
flexor digiti terti perforatus et perforans	flexor per-forans and perforatus digiti III		flexor per-forans et perforatus digiti III		flexor digitus perforatus et perforans digiti terti (intermediate digital flexor)	flexor perfo-ratus medius secundus pedis
flexor digitorum pedis profundus	flexor digitorum longus	flexor profundus	flexor digi-torum longus		flexor digitus perforans	flexor perforans digitorum pro-fundus

flexor digitorum pedis superficialis			superficial digital flexor
1. flexor digiti quarti perforatus		1. flexor perforatus digiti II	1. flexor perforatus indicis primis pedis
2. flexor digiti secundi perforatus		2. flexor perforatus digiti III	2. flexor perforatus medius primis pedis
3. flexor digiti terti perforatus		3. flexor perforatus digiti IV	3. flexor perforatus annularis primis pedis
flexor et abductor digiti quarti manus	flexor brevis digiti III	flexor brevis digiti III	flexor minimi digiti brevis
flexor hallucis brevis	flexor hallucis brevis	flexor hallucis brevis	flexor brevis hallucis
flexor hallucis longus	flexor hallucis longus	flexor hallucis longus	flexor longus hallucis
flexor metacarpi brevis	flexor metacarpi brevis		extensor of the 3rd digiti
flexor metacarpi caudalis	flexor metacarpi posterior	flexor metacarpi posterior	

157

Table I - Bird Muscle Synonomies (continued)

Harvey, Kaiser, Rosenberg	George + Berger	Romer	Fisher	Howell	Chamberlain	Shufeldt
flexor metacarpi longus	flexor metacarpi radialis		flexor meta-carpus radialis		ulnaris lateralis	flexor metacarpus radialis
gastrocnemius 1. caput caudale 2. caput craniale 3. caput mediale	gastro-cnemius	1. gastro-cnemius internus 2. gastro-cnemius externus	gastrocnemius		gastrocnemius	gastrocnemius
gemellus	gemellus	part of ischio-femoralis	obturator externus		gamelli	gamellus
geniohyoideus	geniohyoideus				hyomandibu-laris II	geniohyoideus
gluteus medius	gluteus medius	iliofemo-ralis externus	gluteus profundus	gluteus profundus	gluteus medius	gluteus medius
gluteus minimus	gluteus minimus	iliotro-chantericus	iliacus	iliacus	gluteus pro-fundus	gluteus minimus
gluteus primus	gluteus primus	iliofibu-laris	extensor iliotibialis lateralis	extensor iliotibialis lateralis	tensor fasciae latae	gluteus primus

gluteus superficialis	piriformis	piriformis	piriformis	gluteus superficialis	
hyoideus transversus				hyoideus transversus	
iliacus	iliacus	psoas	psoas	iliacus	
interarticulares	interartibulares				interarticulares
intercostales externales	intercostales externus			external intercostals	external set
intercostales internales	intercostales internus			internal intercostals	internal set
intercostales superficiales				costouncinate ligament	appendico-costales
interosseus dorsalis	interosseus dorsalis	interosseus dorsalis		interosseus dorsalis	interosseus dorsalis
interosseus ventralis	interosseus ventralis	interosseus palmaris		interosseus ventralis	interosseus palmaris
interspinales caudales	interspinales	interspinales			
interspinales craniales	interspinales			interspinales	

Table I - Bird Muscle Synonomies (continued)

Harvey, Kaiser, Rosenberg	George + Berger	Romer	Fisher	Howell	Chamberlain	Shufeldt
intertransversales	intertrans-versarii				intertrans-versales	intertrans-versales
ischiofemoralis minimus	ischio-femoralis	ischio-femoralis	caudofemo-ralis	caudofemo-ralis	cruratus caudalis	femoro-caudal
latissimus dorsi	latissimus dorsi	latissimus dorsi	latissimus dorsi	latissimus dorsi	latissimus dorsi	latissimus dorsi
levator caudae	levator coccygis		levator coccygis		levator coccygeus	levator coccygis
levator rectricum	levator caudae		levator caudae			levator caudae
levatores costarum	levator costarum				levatores costari	levatores costarum
longi colli ventrales	longus colli ventralis				semispinalis capitis	longus colli anterior
longissimus dorsi	longissimus dorsi				longissimus dorsi (illiocostalis)	longissimus dorsi
longus colli dorsalis	longus colli posticus				longus colli	longus colli posticus
longus colli ventralis caudalis						longus colli anterior
longus colli ven-tralis cranialis	longus colli ven-tralis anterior					

longus colli ventralis   pterygoideus internus

longus colli ventralis medialis

mandibularis infraorbitalis

mandibulo-palatinus

mylohyoideus   mylohyoideus   mylo-hyoideus

obliqui colli   multifidus cervicis   obliquus colli

obliquospinales

obliquo-transversales   obliquo-transversales   obliquo-transversales

obliquus capitis caudalis

Table I - Bird Muscle Synonymies (continued)

Harvey, Kaiser, Rosenberg	George + Berger	Romer	Fisher	Howell	Chamberlain	Shufeldt
obliquus internus abdominis	obliquus internus abdominis				obliquus abdominis internus	obliquus internus abdominis
obliquus oculi dorsalis	obliquus superior	superior oblique			obliquus oculi dorsalis	obliquus superior
obliquus oculi ventralis	obliquus inferior	inferior oblique			obliquus oculi ventralis	obliquus inferior
obturator externus	obturator externus	obturator externus	obturator externus		obturator externus	gemellus
obturator internus	obturator internus	part of ischio-femoralis	obturator internus	obturator	obturator internus	obturator internus
patagialis	patagialis		1. tensor patagii brevis 2. tensor patagii longus	1. deltoideus superficial layer	1. patagialis brevis 2. patagialis longus 3. patagialis accessorius	1. tensor patagii brevis 2. tensor patagii longus
pectoralis profundus	pectoralis	supracoracoideus		coracobrachialis	pectoralis profundus (subclavis)	pectoralis secundus

pectoralis super-ficialis	pectoralis super-ficialis	pectoralis super-ficialis	pectoralis super-ficialis	pectoralis super-ficialis	pectoralis super-ficialis	pectoralis major
peroneus brevis	perioneus brevis	peroneus brevis	peroneus brevis		peroneus tertius	tibialis posticus
peroneus longus	peroneus longus	peroneus longus	peroneus longus		peroneus longus	peroneus longus
popliteus	popliteus	popliteus	popliteus		popliteus	
pronator brevis	pronator brevis		pronator brevis		pronator longus brevis	pronator brevis
pronator longus	pronator longus		pronator longus		pronator longus brevis	pronator longus
pterygomandi-bularis						pterygoideus externus
pyramidalis oculi	pyramidalis nictitantis				pyramidalis oculi	pyramidalis nictitantis
quadratomandi-bularis					quadratomandi-bularis	
quadratus oculi	quadratus nictitantis				quadratus oculi	quadratus nictitantis

Table I - Bird Muscle Synonomies (continued)

Harvey, Kaiser, Rosenberg	George + Berger	Romer	Fisher	Howell	Chamberlain	Shufeldt
rectus abdominis	rectus abdominis				rectus abdominis	rectus abdominis
rectus capitis dorsalis	rectis capitis posticus				rectus capitis dorsalis major	rectus capitis posticus major
rectus capitis lateralis	rectus capitis lateralis				rectus capitis lateralis	rectus capitis lateralis
rectus capitis ventralis	rectus capitis ventralis				rectus capitis ventralis major	rectus capitis anticus minor
rectus oculi caudalis	rectus externus	posterior rectus			rectus oculi lateralis	rectus externus
rectus oculi cranialis	rectus internus	anterior rectus			rectus oculi medialis	rectus internus
rectus oculi dorsalis	rectus superior	superior rectus			rectus oculi dorsalis	rectus superior
rectus oculi ventralis	rectus inferior	inferior rectus			rectus oculi ventralis	rectus oculi inferior

rhomboideus	rhomboideus profundus et superficialis	rhomboideus profundus	rhomboideus profundus	rhomboideus	rhomboideus
sacrolumbalis	longissimus dorsi			longissimus dorsi (iliocostalis)	sacro-lumbalis
sartorius	sartorius	extensor iliotibialis anterior	extensor iliotibialis anterior	sartorius	sartorius
scalenius	scalenius			1. scalenius medius 2. scalenius dorsalis	scalenius medius
scapulohumeralis maximus	scapulo-humeralis posterior; subcoraco-scapularis / scapulo-humeralis posterior	deltoideus minor	deltoideus deep brevis	spinatus	scapulo-humeralis
scapulohumeralis minimus	scapulo-humeralis anterior	proscapulo-humeralis brevis	proscapulo-humeralis brevis	subscapularis	teres minor
semimembranosus	semimem-branosus / ischio-flexorius	flexor cruris medialis	flexor cruris medialis	semitendinosus	semimem-branosus

Table I - Bird Muscle Synonomies (continued)

Harvey, Kaiser, Rosenberg	George + Berger	Romer	Fisher	Howell	Chamberlain	Shufeldt
semitendinosus	semitendinosus	ischio-flexorius	flexor cruris lateralis 1. proximal accessory head 2. distal accessory head	flexor cruris lateralis	semimembranosus	semi-tendinosus
semitendinosus accessorius	semitendinosus accessory	ischio-flexorius	flexor cruris lateralis 1. proximal accessory head			accessory pant.
serratus dorsalis	serratus anterior				serratus dorsalis	serratus parvus
serratus magnus					serratus ventralis caudal part	serratus anticus magnus
serratus ventralis	serratus ventralis				serratus ventralis cranial part	serratus parvuus anticus

sphincter ani			sphincter ani	
sternocoracoideus	sterno-coracoideus	sternocora-coideus	sternocora-coideus	subclavius
sternocostales				
sternothyrohyoideus	sternothy-rohyoideus		sternothyro-hyoideus	cleido-trachealis
sternotrachealis	sternotra-chealis		sternotrach-ealis	sterno-trachealis
subcoracoideus	subcora-coideus	subcoracoi-deus		coraco-brachiales
subcostales			subcostals	triangularis sterni
subscapularis	subscapu-laris	proscapulo-humeralis	subscapularis	supra-spinatus
supinator brevis	supinator brevis	supinator brevis	1. supinator lateralis 2. supinator medialis	supinator brevis

Table I - Bird Muscle Synonomies (continued)

Harvey, Kaiser, Rosenberg	George + Berger	Romer	Fisher	Howell	Chamberlain	Shufeldt
temporalis et masseter					1. temporal 2. masseter	1. temporal 2. masseter
tensor patagii caudalis	tensor patagii				expansor secundarium	
tensor patagii longus	tensor patagi longus		tensor patagii longus		patagialis longus (brachiora-dialis)	tensor patagii longus
teres	scapulo-humeralis anterior	scapulo-humeralis anterior	dorsalis scapulae	dorsalis scapulae	teres major	teres et infra-spinatus
thyrobasihyal	sterno-hyoideus				thyroento-glossum	sterno-hyoideus
tibialis caudalis	tibialis posticus	tibialis posticus	peroneus brevis		tibialis caudalis	tibialis posticus
tibialis cranialis	tibialis anterior	tibialis anterior	tibialis anterior		tibialis cranialis	tibialis anticus
trachelomastoideus					trachelomas-toideus	trachelo-mastoideus
tracheolateralis	tracheo-lateralis				ypsilotra-chealis (trachialis lateralis)	tracheo-lateralis
transversus abdominis	transversus abdominis	transversus abdominis			transversus abdominis	transversus abdominis

transversus perinei	transversus perinei		transversus perinei			transversus perinei
trapezius			rhomboideus super-ficialis	rhomboideus super-ficialis	trapezius	trapezius
				rhomboideus super-ficialis	rhomboideus super-ficialis	
triceps 1. caput dorsale 2. caput inernale 3. caput ventrale	triceps 1. brachii 2. coracoidus 3. cubiti	triceps	triceps 1. external head 2. scapular head	triceps	triceps (long, medial, lateral heads)	triceps

*Explanation of the Table

Synonyms are not presented except where the muscle named and described for the turkey was similar to the muscle named in the references cited. In a number of instances, the study cited was concerned with only specific areas of another bird; therefore, no muscles comparable to the turkey were described. It should also be noted that no attempt was made in our study to determine muscle homologies.

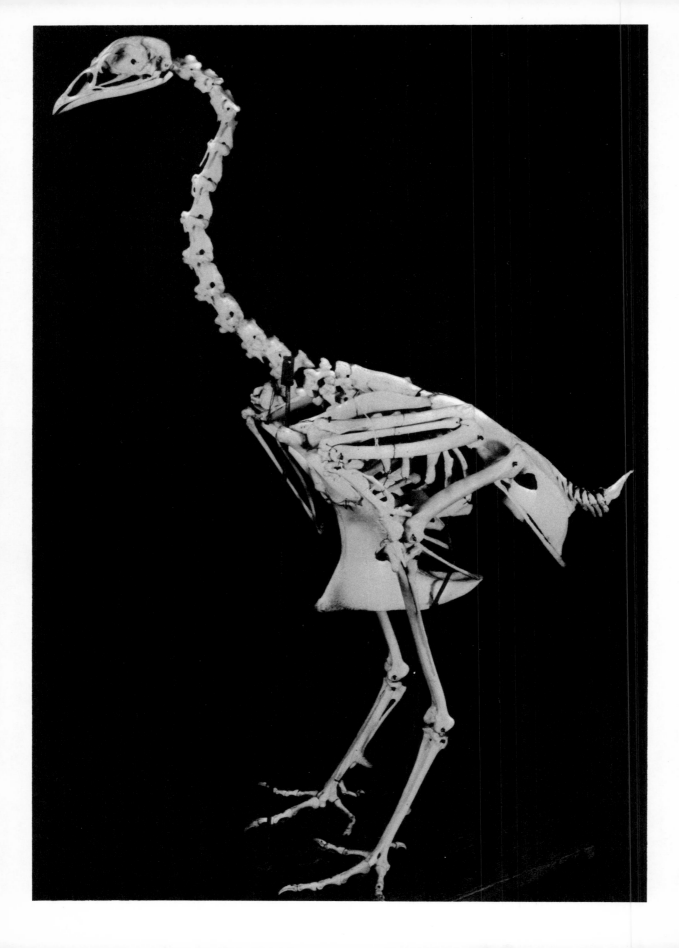

B. Osteology

1. Significant Feature of the Turkey Skeleton

The skeletal elements of the domestic turkey do not differ signifi-
cantly from that of the rock dove (Columba livia) described by
George and Berger (1966) nor that of the chicken as shown by
Chamberlain (1943). Shufeldt (1887) has described in detail the
skeleton of the oscellated turkey and compared the skulls of
the domestic turkey with that of Meleagris g silvestris.

The purpose of this presentation is, therefore, to describe the
characteristics of the turkey skeleton that clearly identifies
this bird as a member of the gallinaceous birds. The excellent
presentation of George and Berger (1966) for the rock dove both
as to the order of presentation and context leads us to follow
their presentation and as a result to borrow heavily from the
facts they have gathered through their detailed search of the
original literature.

The domestic turkey is not generally considered a flying bird.
Nevertheless, the domestic turkey is derived from the wild turkey
which possessed a good ability to fly. All turkeys can fly and
do perch at night.

The selection that has occurred in the domestication of the
turkey has not resulted in loss or significant alteration of
the characteristics that are used in taxonomic studies of birds.
However, it should be pointed out here that the skulls of the
domestic turkeys from which our drawings were taken are far less
angular than the skull of the domestic turkey from which
Shufeldt made his drawings (1887a). In that paper Shufeldt
pointed, however, that the skull of the domestic turkey in
his hands was still less angular than that of the wild turkey.
To determine the full impact that selection has had on the
skeletal structures in the process of domestication would demand
a highly sophisticated study utilizing quantitative evaluations.
Though general agreement has been reached on the proper
terminology of the skeleton and its parts, much needs to be
done on the embryonic origin of the bones, detailed studies of
the reptilian skeleton, and functional comparisons within the
bird groups before agreement will be reached on a standard of
nomenclature.

The adaptive significance of pneumitization in bones of turkeys
has not been fully determined nor has a comparative study of
the rate of closure of skull sutures been done. Indeed, it
has not yet been fully agreed whether the 15th vertebra is the
last of the cervicals or the first of the thoracics nor has it
been determined if gallinaceous bird lose the first digit of
the manus during development (Montagna 1945, George and Berger
1966).

Skull (Pls. 60-63)

The brain case of the turkey skull is composed of the occipital, parietal, frontal, temporal bones and the sphenoidal complex. In the adult bird these are fused. In the 14 month bird, however, sutures between these are clearly evident.

The orbits are separated by a thin bony interorbital septum. In the case of the turkey a well-developed lacrimal bone (Pl. 60-63) has a dorsocaudal projection that extends the supraorbital ridge dorsally and laterally, whereas, a ventrocaudal process extends into the orbit to which fascia that encompasses a well-developed lacrimal gland adheres.

The external nares are bounded by the premaxilla, nasals, and maxilla which form the facial portion of the turkey skull. The nostrils open externally, thus, are pervious. The nares are separated by a nasal septum that extends from the nasal capsule cranially to the ethmoid caudally; and from the nasal process of the premaxilla dorsally and to the vomer ventrally.

The maxilla, as described by us, is the cranial bone of the zygomatic. Many ornithologists, however, consider the premaxillae as the "upper mandibles" or maxillae. In some birds these are capable of some extension and flexion (kinetic) by way of a transverse craniofacial or nasafrontal hinge (the articulation with the cephalic edge of the frontals). Nevertheless, neither the maxilla as we identify it nor the premaxilla (upper mandibles) in the turkey are kinetic in the adult turkey.

Vertebral Column and Ribs (Pls. 65-71)

For purposes of descriptions we have preferred retention of the terms, cervical, thoracic, lumbosacral, sacral, synsacral, and caudal vertebrae including the pygostyle.

There are 14 cervical vertebrae including the atlas and axis in the turkey. In the several skeletons we studied, there was no variation in this number. The cervical vertebrae each have distinctive characteristics that would permit a careful student of osteology to distinguish each from the other. The 14th cervical vertebra does not have a free (asternal) rib as described for the chicken. The 15th vertebra in the turkey has a free rib and has been included as the first thoracic vertebra in our study.

We prefer to classify the 15th vertebra as a thoracic vertebra since it does have ribs that articulate freely

172

on parapophyses characteristic of thoracic vertebrae; whereas, "ribs" on cervical vertebrae are firmly fused and are much reduced in the 13th and 14th cervicals. The free rib, therefore, of the 15th vertebra cannot at this point be homologized with the fused ribs of the cervical vertebrae. This question cannot be resolved without more comparative anatomical research in birds.

Notarium (Pls. 69-71)

There are seven thoracic vertebrae in the turkey. The first and sixth articulate freely and have asternal ribs, whereas, the second through the fourth are fused to each other at their processes as in the chicken and rock dove. The seventh thoracic vertebra is fused to the first lumbar vertebra at the centrum and to the ilium dorsally and by transverse processes laterally. An asternal rib is fused to the seventh thoracic vertebra.

The lumbar and sacral vertebrae are fused and are, therefore, considered as the lumbosacral vertebrae.

The lumbar vertebrae (vertebrae lumbales) probably four in number, are fused to each other and to the ilium.

The sacral vertebrae form the caudal fourth of the pelvic roof as a result of fusion of their dorsal spines and transverse processes.

The six synsacral vertebrae form the caudal three-fourths of the pelvic girdle and are fused laterally by their transverse processes to the medial borders of the ischii.

The sixth synsacral vertebra is fused to the first caudal vertebra by cartilage in the mature bird.

The turkey has six or seven free caudal vertebrae including a pygostyle. This number varies even between individuals. According to George and Berger (1966) the numbers of cervical and thoracic vertebrae, however, remain relatively constant within a species.

Pelvic Girdle (Pls. 69-71)

The synsacrum is fused with the ilium and ischium to form a rigid pelvic girdle in the turkey. The pelvic bones are fused cranially with the ischii. A long narrow ischiopubic foramen (fenestra) lies between the two points of contact of the ischium and pubic bones. An obturator foramen is formed similarly but is cranial to the elongate ischiopubic fenestra.

A well-developed <u>iliopectineal</u> process is present cranial and ventral to the <u>acetabulum</u>.

The neural canals in the pelvic girdle are formed by fusion of the dorsomedial borders of the <u>ilium</u> and the <u>synsacral</u> <u>vertebrae</u> (fused lumbars and sacral vertebrae).

<u>Pectoral Girdle</u> (Pls. 72-75)

The pectoral girdle of turkeys is composed of the typical three bones: <u>scapula</u>, <u>coracoid</u>, and <u>furcula</u>.

The <u>scapula</u> is flat and thin and extends parallel to the <u>thoracic</u> vertebrae. It articulates with the <u>coracoid</u> and is attached to the free dorsal ends of the <u>furcula</u> by ligaments. The <u>coracoids</u> and <u>furcula</u> are not fused to each other. A reduced <u>hypocleideum</u> is formed by fusion of the <u>clavicles</u> in the turkey.

A foramen tiosseum is formed by the dorsal apposition (articulation) of the head of the <u>scapula</u>, <u>coracoid</u>, and <u>furcula</u>.

Both the <u>scapula</u> and <u>coracoids</u> have well-developed pneumatic foramen in which there are extensive air sacs.

<u>Sternum</u> (Pls. 74-75)

The turkey like most carinates has a ventrally directed <u>keel</u> or <u>carina sterni</u>. Extending caudally from the <u>sternum</u> is a single median <u>xiphoid</u> <u>process</u> (<u>metasternum</u>), two <u>caudolateral</u> processes, and two <u>dorsolateral</u> processes. The turkey, therefore, has two lateral notches but does not have a posteriomedial fenestra as reported by George and Berger (1966) for <u>Columba</u> <u>livia</u>.

<u>Hind Limb</u> (Pls. 76-81)

The hind limb of the turkey consists of a <u>femur</u>, <u>tibiotarsus</u>, <u>patella</u>, <u>tarsometatarsus</u>, and four <u>digits</u>.

The <u>femur</u> is pneumatized from the large abdominal air sacs. The <u>tibia</u> is well developed in the turkey but distally is a composite of the tibia and tarsal bones. The <u>fibula</u> on the other hand is poorly developed. It does have a well-developed head that articulates with the femur and the head of the <u>tibia</u> proximally. The <u>fibula</u> extends about three-fourths the length of the <u>tibia</u> and is styliform at its distal end.

The <u>tarsometatarsus</u> is formed by fusion of the distal <u>tarsals</u> with three metatarsals. George and Berger (1966) report

that an independent first metatarsal articulates with the
medial border of the tarsometatarsus. In addition to a
free metatarsal I, the turkey has a well-developed
hypotarsal sesamoid that is in close apposition with the
medial trochlea of the tarsometatarsus.

The male turkey has a well-developed spur at the distal
end of the hypotarsal styliform process. The spur is
absent in the female; nevertheless, the hypotarsal
styliform process is well developed in the female.

The hallux of the turkey points obliquocaudally and has
one phalanx plus an ungal phalanx. The first phalanx
articulates with the free metatarsal I. Digit II points
obliquomedially and has two phalanges and an ungus.
Digit III, the heaviest of the digits, points cranially
and is composed of three heavy bodied phalanges and an
ungus. Digit IV is pointed craniolaterally and is composed
of four phalanges and one ungus. With this configuration
the turkey foot may be considered anisodactyle and to be
typical of the perching foot.

The Wing Bones (Pls. 83-85)

The humerus is pneumatic in the turkey as in nearly all
birds and has a single pneumatic foramen for an air chamber
from the interclavicular air sac.

The ulna is characteristically longer and heavier than
the radius. The first carpometacarpus is separated from
the distal ends of the ulna and radius by two free carpal
bones; the radiale (scapholunar) and ulnare (cuneiform).
The remaining carpals are fused with the proximal ends of
the three metacarpals of the manus.

Although birds characteristically have three metacarpals,
in the adult turkey metacarpal II is fused with carpal II
and does not form a distinctive process.

We have followed Montagna (1945), Holmgren (1955), and
Fisher and Goodman (1955) in our labeling of the metacarpals
and digits of the hand as II, III, and IV. There is
embryological evidence that metacarpals II, III, and IV,
as well as Digits II, III, and IV only, are retained after
hatching. George and Berger (1966), however, cast some
doubt on this conclusion.

Digits II and IV of the turkey have one phalanx as in most
birds, and Digit III has two phalanges.

Plates 60-63   Skull (Male)   Right Lateral, Dorsal
                                            Ventral, and Caudal Views

Ethmoid

The ethmoid is the most medial of the cranial bones and its caudal
region forms the mediocranial border of the cranium. It is bounded
dorsally by the frontal, dorsolaterally by the orbital plates of
the frontal, and by the caudal portion of the nasal. Cranially it
is bounded by the vomer and ventrally by the rostrum of the basisphenoid. Its lateral borders are bounded caudally by the medial
borders of the alisphenoid and presphenoid.

  b. The splenial is thin and flat and lies medially on the
      mandibular complex and overlays the caudal projections of
      the pars dentalis.

  c. The pars supraangularis projects into the bifurcation of
      the pars dentalis and lies dorsal on the mandible. The
      coronoid process lies dorsally on the supraangularis just
      cranial to the articular facet of the pars articularis.

  d. The pars articularis is distinguished by two processes and
      the mandibular condyle. The mandibular condyle articulates
      with the ventral process of the quadrate. The caudal proc-
      ess of the pars articularis extends toward the median line
      of the basitemporal plate from the mandibular condyle.

  e. The pars angularis is thin and lies ventral to the pars
      articularis and supraangularis. Its caudal region forms
      the ventral surface of the mandibular process.

Frontal

Position: The frontals lie between the cranial border of the
parietals and the caudal border of the nasals and touches the
temporal at the caudal border of the supraorbital process. The
cranial borders of the frontals extend to the dorsal and medial
aspect of the nasal processes of the premaxilla and the cranial
aspect of the supraorbital processes. The frontals also touch
the orbital processes of the lachrymals. A portion of the frontal
(orbital plate) forms the roof and the caudal aspect of the orbital
fossa. The orbital plate meets with the alisphenoid in the caudal
aspect of this fossa. In the median line dorsally, the right and
left orbital plates meet the ethmoid bone of the facial group.

In the three-month bird the right and left frontals are separated
by the frontal suture. The sphenofrontal suture clearly sepa-
rates the alisphenoid and the frontal in the caudal orbital region.
In the fifteen-month bird these sutures are not visible.

At the junction of the orbital fundus with the orbital plate of
the frontal are two foramina through which the first and second
divisions of the trigeminal nerve pass. At the junction of the
orbital fundus and orbital plate are two other foramina. The
more cranial and larger is the olfactory foramen, and just caudal
to this foramen, about four mm., is the trochlear nerve foramen.

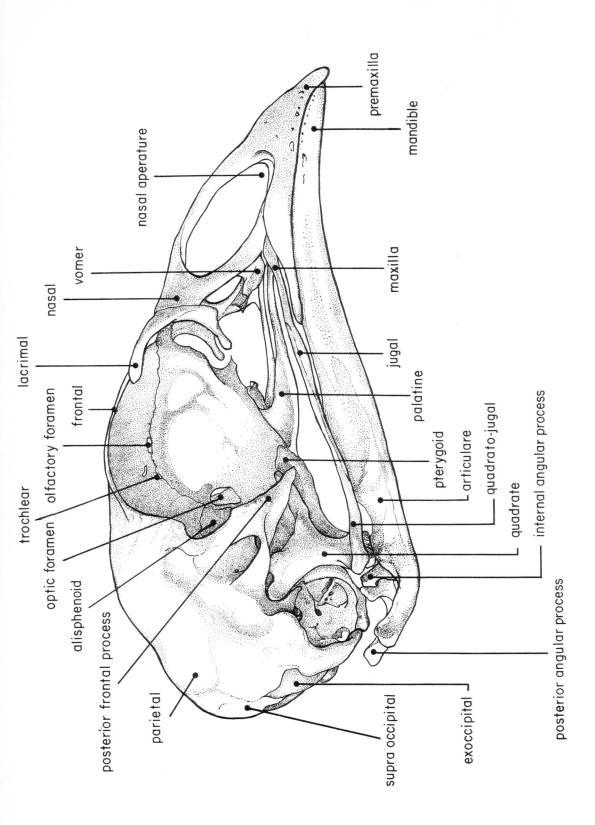

nasal aperature

premaxilla

mandible

vomer

nasal

maxilla

lacrimal

frontal

jugal

palatine

trochlear

olfactory foramen

optic foramen

pterygoid

articulare

quadrato-jugal

alisphenoid

quadrate

internal angular process

posterior frontal process

parietal

supra occipital

exoccipital

posterior angular process

SKULL (MALE)–RIGHT–LATERAL VIEW
PLATE 60

The optic foramen is in the same vicinity and is the largest in
the orbital region. Ventral to it are two or three (variable)
nutrient foramina at the sutures of the ethmoid, alisphenoid, and
presphenoid.

Lacrimal
The lacrimal is one of three facial bones: the lacrimal, nasal,
and premaxilla and forms the dorsocranial limit of the orbit. Its
body articulates broadly with the nasal and narrowly with the
frontals. The distinctive feature of the lacrimals are the dorsal
and ventral orbital processes. The dorsal process extends caudally
and somewhat laterally and thereby enlarges the orbit. The ventral
process extends mediocaudally into the orbit.

Mandible
The mandible, the most ventral bone of the facial group, forms the
apex of the ventral beak and extends to the auditory meatus.

This bone is composed of five embryonic units that are fused in a
fifteen-month bird, but in the three-month bird these are still
distinguishable.

   a. The pars dentalis forms the lower beak, from which ex-
      tends the right and left caudal projections. In its
      medial aspect there is a "tongue-and-groove" union
      with the splenial dorsally, and with the pars supra-
      angularis, and the pars dentalis laterally.

Nasal
The nasal is bounded caudally by the frontal, laterally by the
lacrimal, and medially by the nasal process of the premaxilla.
Ventrally it touches the maxilla, premaxilla, and palatine. It
is composed of a body, caudalis processus frontalis, from which
two processes extend: the processus intermaxillaris and processus
maxillaris cranialis. The three processes form the caudal, lat-
teral, and medial borders of the external nares. The body is convex laterally and concave toward the median line. Its caudal border is separated from the frontal by the nasofrontal suture and
lies on the dorsal surface of the ethmoid.

Nasal septum
The nasal septum is in the median aspect of the nasal aperature.
Its caudal border meets the ventral process of the ethmoid, and
is bounded by the ethmoid caudally, the vomer ventrally, the
oblique process of the vomer cranially, and dorsally by the caudal fourth of the nasal process of the premaxilla.

The cranial half of the nasal septum is bounded by the nasal capsule, the nasal process of the premaxilla and the oblique process
of the vomer.

Occipital
The occipital is the most caudal bone of the cranium and is
bounded dorsally and cranially by the caudal border of the parietals, laterally by the caudal border of the temporal (squamosal),
and ventrally by the caudal border of the basisphenoid (basitemporal plate).

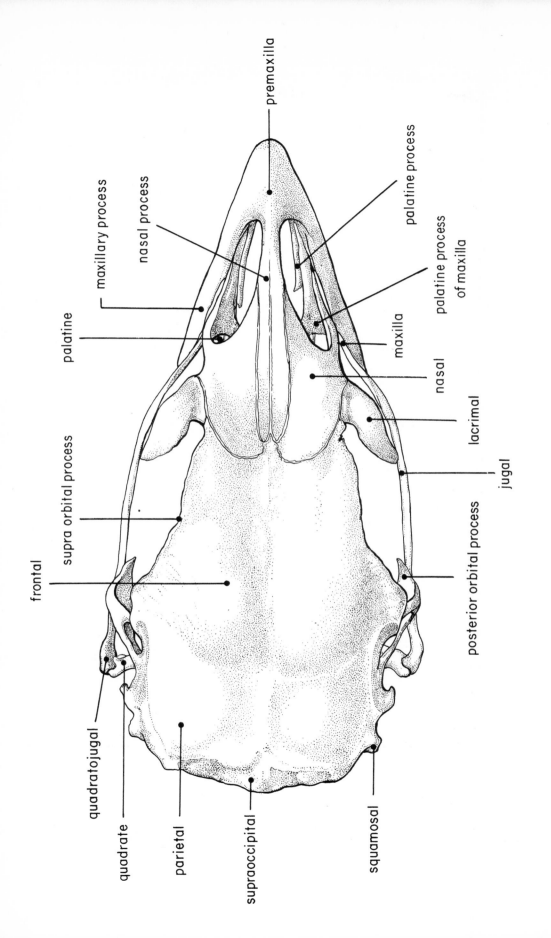

premaxilla

palatine process

palatine process
of maxilla

maxillary process

nasal process

palatine

maxilla

nasal

lacrimal

jugal

supra orbital process

frontal

posterior orbital process

quadratojugal

quadrate

parietal

supraoccipital

squamosal

SKULL – (MALE) – DORSAL VIEW

PLATE 61

From a caudal view of the cranium, the occipital forms an arc from dorsal to about two-thirds ventral, at which point it becomes variously shaped to help form the lateroventrally placed foramen lacerum. The foramen magnum is centrally located in this bone.

Ventral to the foramen magnum is a single occipital condyle that articulates with the atlas. During extreme flexion of the skull, a subcondyloid fossa ventral to the base of the occipital condyle receives the body of the atlas.

There are two pairs of occipital foramen lateral to the occipital condyle; the spinal accessory nerve foramen and the foramen lacerum lateral to these.

In the three-month turkey it is possible to distinguish the four bones from which the occipital has been derived: a supra-occipital dorsal, two exoccipitals lateral and a basioccipital ventral to the foramen magnum.

Palatine

The palatine is long and thin. The caudal triangular process is convex dorsally and concave ventrally and articulates medially with the rostrum of the basisphenoid.

Caudally, the palatine articulates with the medial articular surface of the pterygoid and cranially with the dorsal surface of the palatine process of the premaxilla. The caudal fifth of the palatine articulates with the rostrum of the basisphenoid medially and laterally with the superior maxilla and the maxillary process of the premaxilla.

Parietal

The parietals are quadrilateral in shape. These two bones (fused in the fifteen-month bird) are the most caudal of the dorsal bones of the cranium. They are bounded cranially by the frontals, laterally by the temporals, and caudally by the dorsal border of the occipital. In the fifteen-month bird it is difficult to see the demarcation between the parietals, frontals and the temporal (squamosal) bones. A sagital depression marks where the fusion of the interparietals has occurred.

In the three-month bird the parietals are separated from the frontals, temporals and the occipital by the coronal sutures cranially, the squamosal sutures laterally, the lambdoidal sutures caudally and the interparietal suture medially. The frontal fontanel and occipital fontanel may still be seen and the interparietals are not yet completely incorporated into the parietals.

Premaxilla

The premaxilla forms the upper beak and the cranial border of the nasal aperture. It has three pairs of processes that project caudally:

a. The nasal process is biramous, extends to the frontal and overlays the ethmoid and is bounded laterally by the nasal.

b. The maxillary process meets with the maxillary process of the nasal medially and the cranial extensions of the palatine and maxilla at its caudal limit. The maxilla and

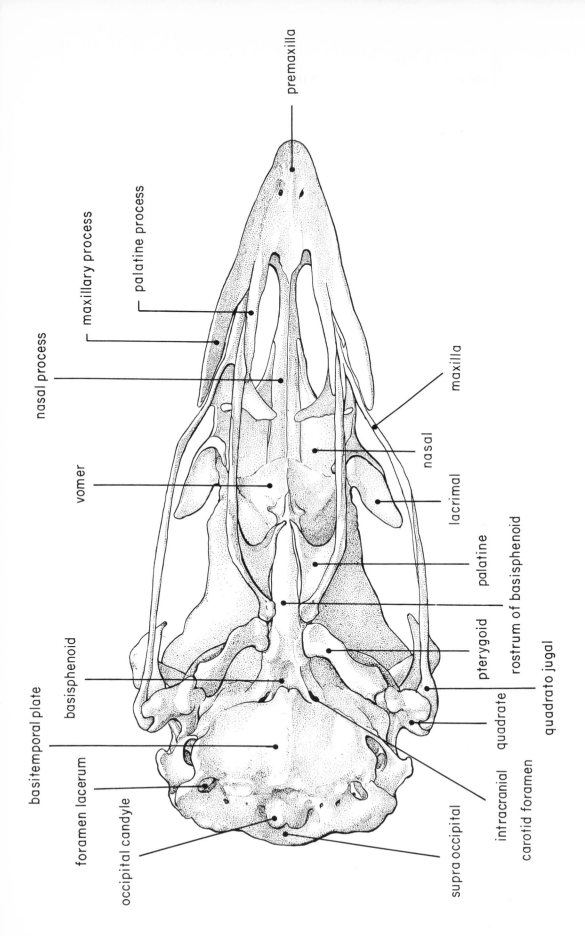

premaxilla

maxillary process

palatine process

nasal process

vomer

maxilla

nasal

lacrimal

palatine

rostrum of basisphenoid

pterygoid

quadrato jugal

basisphenoid

basitemporal plate

foramen lacerum

occipital candyle

quadrate

intracranial

carotid foramen

supra occipital

SKULL – (MALE) – VENTRAL VIEW
PLATE 62

the maxillary process forms the bony support for the upper beak.

    c.   The palatine process projects caudally parallel to the maxillary process but is medial to it. It meets with the cranial projection of the maxilla dorsally and forms a bony support for the "gum" plate of the palate.

The premaxilla forms the cranial border of the external nasal aperature.

Pterygoid
The pterygoid is medial to the quadrate and lies caudoventrally in the orbit. It articulates with the quadrate, the articular process of the basisphenoid, and the caudal limit of the palatine.

Its three articular surfaces are: quadrate articulare on its laterocaudal surface; rostrum articulare on its medial surface; and palatine articulare on its mediocranial surface.

Quadrate
The quadrate is Y-shaped and is the most caudal of the facial bones. Its caudal aspect helps to form the cranial curvature of the external auditory meatus.

Its caudal process projects dorsally and caudally to articulate with the squamous temporal, the cranial process projects mediocranially in a line parallel with that of the pterygoid with which it articulates, and its ventral process articulates with the quadratojugal.

Sphenoid (Sphénoidal complex: basisphenoid, presphenoid and alisphenoid)
The sphenoidal complex is composed of the basisphenoid, presphenoid and alisphenoid.

The caudal portion of the basisphenoid is covered by a broad, bony plate, the basitemporal plate, whereas the rostrum of the basisphenoid extends craniomedially to meet the vomer.

The presphenoid element is dorsal to the basisphenoid and may be seen as the cranial border of the external auditory meatus.

The alisphenoid, as seen in a three-month bird, projects from the presphenoid as a rectangular plate and is in contiguity with the caudoventral border of the orbital plate of the frontal. In the mature bird the points of fusion cannot be distinguished. What has been called the supraorbital process of the frontal is actually a process of the alisphenoid, alae orbitales. We have named this process the zygomatic process of the alisphenoid. This process, however, is composed of much reduced processes from the frontals and temporals.

Temporal
The temporals are bounded caudally by the occipitals, dorsally by the parietals, laterally and ventrally by the quadrates, ventrally by the sphenoids, and cranially they are contiguous with the alisphenoids.

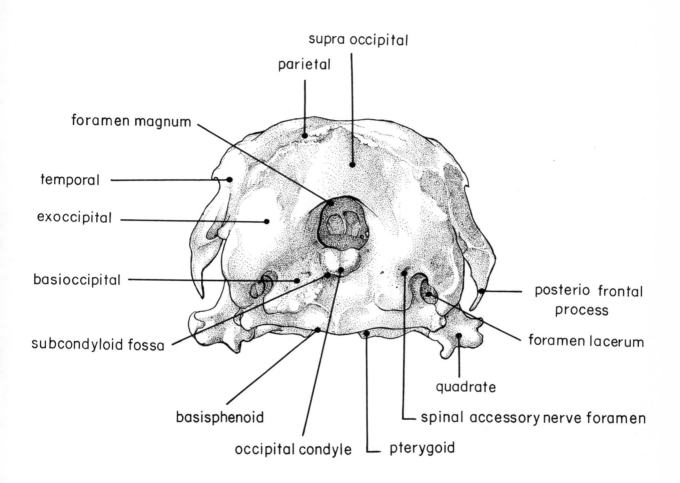

supra occipital

parietal

foramen magnum

temporal

exoccipital

basioccipital

subcondyloid fossa

basisphenoid

occipital condyle

pterygoid

spinal accessory nerve foramen

quadrate

foramen lacerum

posterio frontal process

SKULL – (MALE) – CAUDAL VIEW

PLATE 63

The squamous portion of the temporal forms the lateral wall of the cranium, whereas the petrosal forms the floor. The squamosal and petrosal are fused and contain the auditory structures.

At a point just cranial to the articulation of the temporal with the quadrate, a small osseus process continues as cartilage (zygomatic process of the temporal) to meet with the ossified zygomatic process of the alisphenoid. This cartilage is ossified in the fifteen-month bird. From our observations it would appear that the so-called supra-orbital process of the frontal in birds, at least in the turkey, is actually a process (alae orbitalis) of the alisphenoid. We have therefore called this process the zygomatic process of the alisphenoid.

The external auditory meatus is bounded caudally by the external auditory process of the occipital, ventrally and cranially by the temporal wing of the sphenoid, and dorsally by the squamous temporal.

The foramina observed in the petrous temporal seen by looking into the external auditory meatus are: the foramen lacerum, which is a large cavity, and this is divided into two other cavities deeply. The most ventral of these is the fenestra ovales, through which the columella passes. The most dorsal of the foramina in the auditory meatus is the foramen for the semi-circular canal.

Vomer
The vomer is delicate and lies cranial to the rostrum of the basisphenoid. This bone in the turkey does not have a bony or cartilaginous articulation with the rostrum as in the chicken (Kaupp, 1918). Cranially the vomer articulates with the caudal aspect of the palatine process of the maxilla. The vomer acts as a base for the internasal septum. A dorsocaudal process projects obliquely from the vomer in the caudal third of the nasal aperture to articulate with the ethmoid.

Its main center of ossification is slightly parallelogram in shape, with a short caudal ligamental projection from which strong ligaments connect to the cranial projection of the rostrum.

Zygomatic (jugal, quadratojugal, maxilla)
The zygomatic is a complex of three bones that extend from the ventral process of the quadrate to the maxillary process of the nasal:

   a. The quadratojugal of the zygomatic complex is long and thin.
       At its caudal limit it articulates with the ventral process
       of the quadrate. It extends cranially to about the middle
       of the ventral orbital region where it fuses with the
       caudal projection of the superior maxilla.

   b. The jugal lies dorsally over the cranial projection of the
       quadratojugal and the caudal projection of the "superior"
       maxilla.

   c. The "superior" maxilla extends from the maxillary process
       of the nasal caudally and passes ventral to the jugal and
       articulates with the cranial projection of the quadratojugal.

At its nasal articulation the "superior" maxilla is bounded
ventrally by the maxillary process of the premaxilla. A
palatine process extends medially from the cranial limit
where it forms a part of the caudal floor of the nares.

Plate 64   Hyoid Apparatus   Dorsal, Ventral, and Lateral View

Hyoid Apparatus

The hyoid apparatus lies between the mandibles and is partially embedded in the tongue. It is composed of seven units variously ossified: entoglossum (one unit, cartilaginous); basihyal (one unit, bony); basibranchial (one unit, cartilaginous); ceratobranchial (two units, cartilaginous); and epibranchials (two units, cartilaginous).

The entoglossum is convex dorsally and concave ventrally and lies within the tissue of the tongue. It is "Y" shaped. The tail of the "Y" points in the direction of tongue tip whereas the arms of the "Y" are directed caudally.

The basihyal is the more ossified unit of the apparatus. It is convex on the ventral surface and has a ridge on the dorsal surface medially. It has four articulating surfaces: one cranial for articulation with the entoglossum; one caudal for articulation with the basibranchial; and two caudolaterally for articulation with the ceratobranchial units.

The basibranchial lies on the ventral surface of the superior larynx. It is styliform in shape and directed caudally.

The ceratobranchials lie between the basihyals and the epibranchials. The epibranchials are styliform and directed dorsally. Its union with the ceratobranchial is cartilaginous and is not a free articulation.

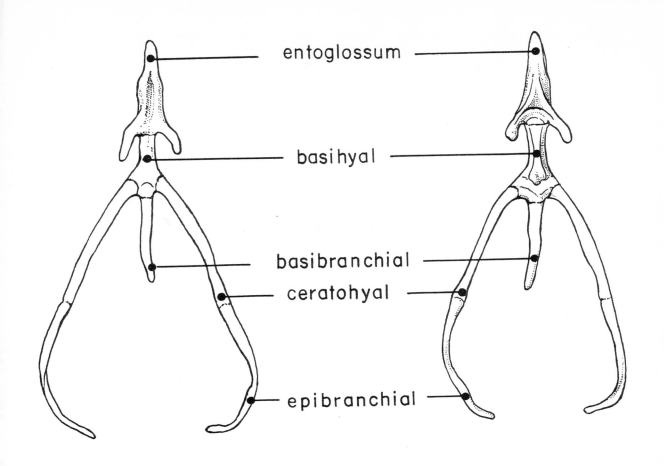

entoglossum

basihyal

basibranchial

ceratohyal

epibranchial

DORSAL VIEW

VENTRAL VIEW

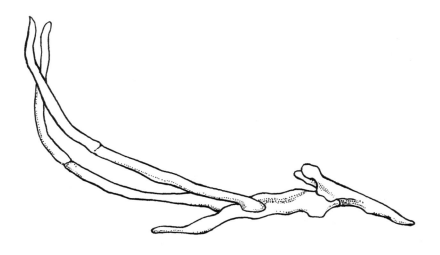

HYOID APPARATUS   RIGHT LATERAL VIEW
PLATE 64

Plate 65   Cervical Vertebrae - Articulated   Left Lateral View

Cervical Vertebrae - Articulated

There are fourteen cervical vertebrae in the turkey. These include the atlas and axis. The first cervical, the atlas, articulates with the occipital condyle, and the fourteenth with the first thoracic vertebra.

The atlas and axis are distinctly different in structure from each other as well as the other cervical vertebrae. The third and fourth cervicals are morphologically similar but differ from the other cervicals in that they possess alar processes between the postzygapophyses and the prezygapophyses. The fifth through the twelfth cervicals have a ventral carotid arch and are thus distinguished from the thirteenth and fourteenth cervicals that lack these.

The thirteenth cervical vertebra has a foramen located ventrally just caudal to its cervical rib base; the fourteenth cervical vertebra, however, lacks this foramen.

Third and Fourth Cervical Vertebrae

These two vertebrae are similar in structure, thus are described together.

A dorsal spine and the prezygapophyses are in the most cranial portion of these vertebrae.

The cranial articular surface is ventral to the neural canal and lateral to these are two intravertebral nutrient foramina.

The diapophysis is just ventral to the prezygapophysis, and the parapophysis lies ventral to the diapophysis. A pleurapophysis (cervical rib) is fused to these tubercles and projects caudally.

The alar processes with large intervetebral foramina lateral to the dorsal spine extend broadly between the prezygapophyses and postzygapophyses.

These vertebrae have the anapophyses dorsal to the postzygapophyses and neuropophyses with an intervertebral notch.

Fifth Cervical Vertebra

The fifth cervical vertebra has a dorsal spine, postzygapophyses and prezygapophyses and a ventral carotid arch. Two intravertebral foramina are lateral to the cranial articular surface.

Thirteenth and Fourteenth Cervical Vertebrae

The thirteenth cervical vertebra is longer than the fourteenth, but the latter is wider and deeper in its cranial aspect with a more pronounced dorsal spine. A carotid arch is absent in these two cervicals, and they have a single ventral spine (hypapophysis).

The tenth through the fourteenth cervical vertebrae have a deep ligamental fovea in the caudal aspect of the dorsal spine for attachment of the intervertebral ligaments. The fourteenth cervical vertebra does not have a free cervical rib as in chickens (Kaupp, 1918).

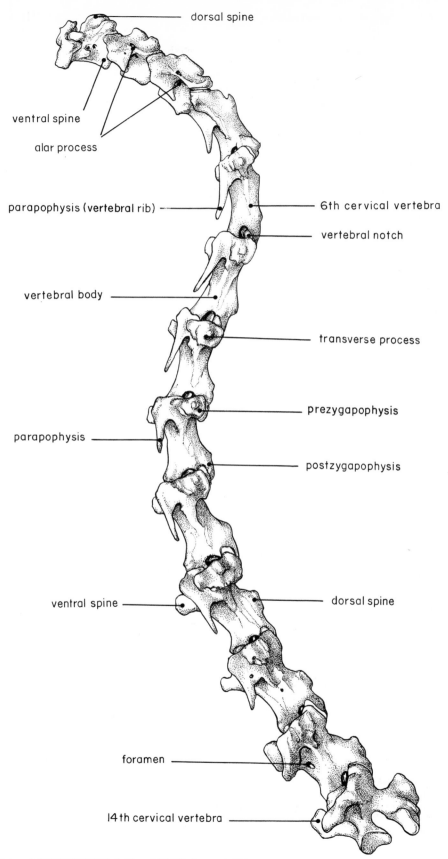

dorsal spine

ventral spine

alar process

parapophysis (**vertebral** rib)

6th cervical vertebra

vertebral notch

vertebral body

transverse process

prezygapophysis

parapophysis

postzygapophysis

ventral spine

dorsal spine

foramen

14th cervical vertebra

CERVICAL VERTEBRAE-ARTICULATED- LEFT-LATERAL VIEW
PLATE 65

Atlas

The atlas, the first cervical vertebra, is ring-shaped and lacks a dorsal spine. The dorsal neural arch, formed by the fused neuropophyses, surrounds the neural canal. An articular facet for the occipital condyle is on its cranial surface ventral to the neural canal. The ventral spine is variable in shape. It may be broadly triangular or have a median and two reduced lateral protuberances.

Three articular surfaces face caudally, two lateral articular facets for the articular processes of the axis and one medial articular facet that articulates with the odontoid process of the axis.

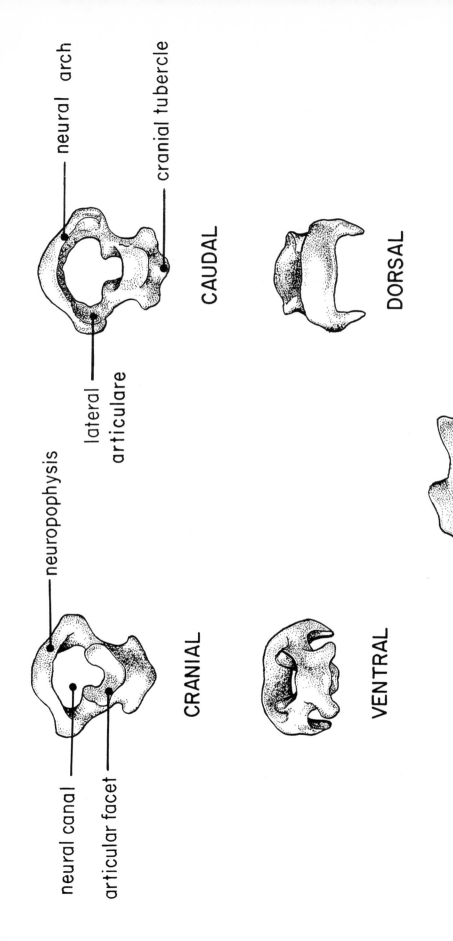

neural arch

neural canal

articular facet

neuropophysis

CRANIAL

cranial tubercle

lateral
articulare

CAUDAL

VENTRAL

DORSAL

postzygapophysis

ATLAS—LEFT LATERAL VIEW
PLATE 66

Plate 67   Axis   Right Lateral View

Axis

The axis, the second cervical vertebra, has a broad neural spine dorsal to the neural arch. Its articular processes (prezygapophyses) face caudolaterally from the roof of the neural arch and articulate with the craniomedially faced articular processes of the atlas. An odontoid process (embryologically the centrum of atlas) projects sufficiently into a facet in the atlas so that it articulates with the occipital condyle.

The cranial articular surface of the centrum is ventral to the odontoid process and articulates with the reduced centrum of the atlas.

The two caudal articular surfaces, postzygopophyses, project laterally and articulate with the prezygapophyses of the third cervical vertebra. An intervertebral notch, an identation of the neurapophysis, lies between the postzygopophyses and the centrum. Its caudal articular surface on the centrum articulates with the cranial articular surface of the third cervical vertebra. The hypapophysis forms a single reduced ventral spine on the centrum.

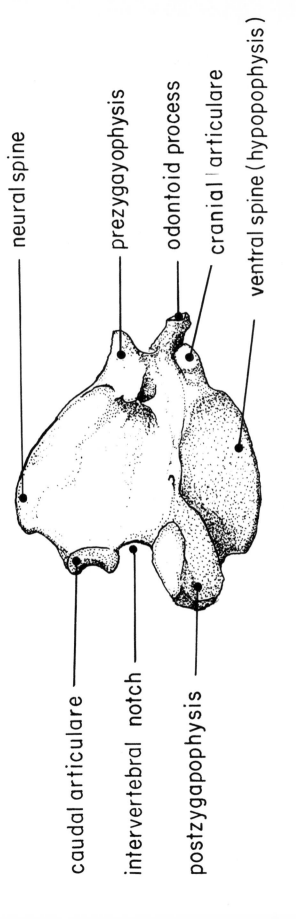

neural spine

prezygayophysis

odontoid process

cranial articulare

ventral spine (hypopophysis)

caudal articulare

intervertebral notch

postzygapophysis

AXIS – RIGHT – LATERAL VIEW

PLATE 67

Sixth through Twelfth Cervical Vertebrae

The sixth through the twelfth cervical vertebrae have a much reduced dorsal spine.

There are two intravertebral foramina lateral to the cranial articulating surface. In the dorsal arch of the intravertebral foramina may be seen nutrient foramina. These vertebrae have fused cervical ribs that project caudally.

The parapophyseal projections that form the carotid arch are more pronounced in each succeeding vertebra to the tenth cervical. The carotid arch is reduced on the eleventh cervical. In the twelfth cervical the two bases of the carotid arch are united, and the arch is reduced to a ventral groove at the cranial end of the hypapophyseal ridge, whereas the anapophysis is more prominent in the more caudal of the cervical vertebrae.

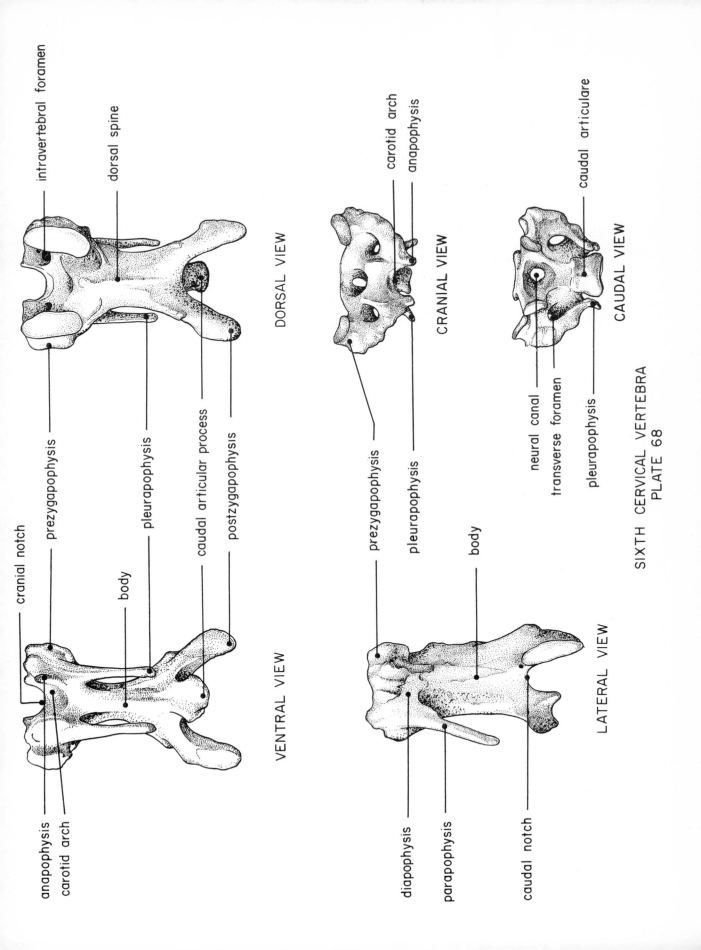

intravertebral foramen

dorsal spine

DORSAL VIEW

cranial notch

prezygapophysis

body

pleurapophysis

caudal articular process

postzygapophysis

anapophysis
carotid arch

VENTRAL VIEW

carotid arch

anapophysis

CRANIAL VIEW

prezygapophysis

pleurapophysis

body

LATERAL VIEW

diapophysis

parapophysis

caudal notch

caudal articulare

CAUDAL VIEW

neural canal

transverse foramen

pleurapophysis

SIXTH CERVICAL VERTEBRA
PLATE 68

Thoracic Vertebrae

The first thoracic vertebra articulates with the fourteenth cervical and
the seventh thoracic vertebra is fused with the first lumbar vertebra.

The first and sixth thoracic vertebra articulate freely, whereas the second
through the fifth are fused (notarium). Seven thoracic ribs articulate
with the seven thoracic vertebrae.

First Thoracic Vertebra

This vertebra has a prominent dorsal spine. The ventral spine is like that
of the fourteenth cervical. The transverse process (an expansion of the
diapophysis) is lateral to the prezygapophysis. The prezygapophyses have
a ventrally-faced costal facet for the articulation with the rib tubercles
of the first thoracic rib.

Second, Third, Fourth and Fifth Thoracic Vertebrae

The dorsal spines, the pre- and postzygapophyses, the cranial and caudal
articular facets and the ventral spines of these vertebrae are fused to
one another. The transverse processes are fused only at their lateral
borders.

Pneumatic foramina are present in the base of the transverse processes of
the first, second, third and fourth thoracic vertebrae.

The cranial border of the ilium lies dorsal to the caudal half of the sixth
thoracic vertebra.

The seventh thoracic vertebra is fused to the first lumbar vertebra. This
vertebra contains all the elements of the other thoracic vertebrae. The
postzygapophyses are fused with the prezygapophyses of the lumbar vertebrae
and the transverse processes are fused laterally and dorsally to the ventral surface of the ilium.

Thoracic Ribs

The seven pairs of thoracic ribs articulate with the thoracic vertebrae.
The five caudal pairs articulate with sternal ribs; the other two pairs
end freely.

The first two thoracic ribs are the false or asternal ribs. The first is
styliform and is the shortest of the ribs. The first rib pair articulates
with the first thoracic vertebra but is sometimes referred to as a cervical
rib. The ribs have two proximal articulating processes: the rib tubercle,
a dorsal process, articulates with costal facet of the diapophysis and the
head of the rib (ventral process) with the costal facet of the parapophysis.

Ribs 2 through 6 also possess uncinate processes which project caudodor-
sally and lie over the next succeeding rib. The uncinate processes arise
from the caudal borders of the ribs about two-thirds distal their vertebral
articulations. The distal ends of these ribs are rounded and touch on a
cartilage pad which acts as an articulation between the thoracic and
sternal ribs.

196

The seventh thoracic rib lacks an uncinate process. Proximally, it articulates with the fused seventh thoracic and first lumbar vertebra. Distally this rib articulates with the fifth (or false) sternal rib.

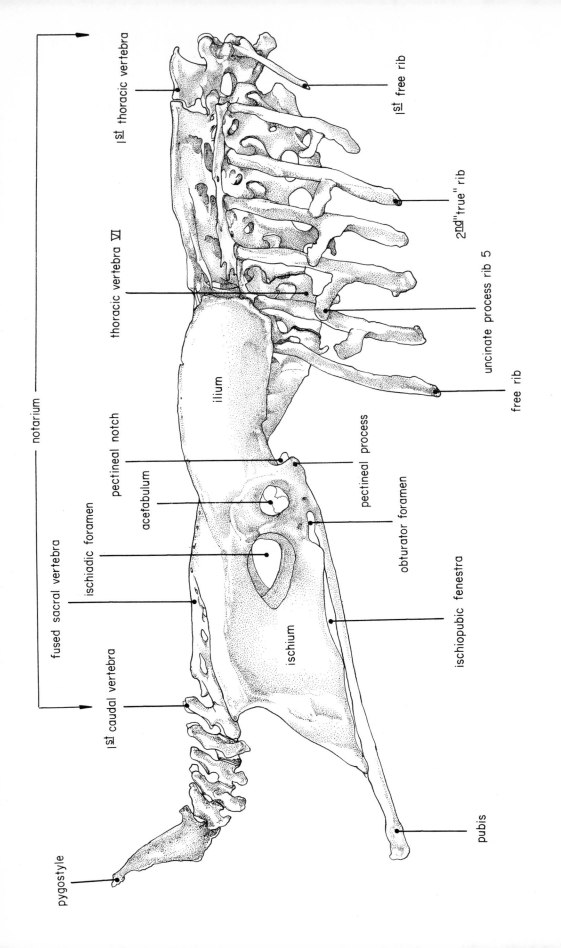

pygostyle

1st caudal vertebra

fused sacral vertebra

notarium

ischiadic foramen

pectineal notch

acetabulum

ilium

thoracic vertebra VI

1st thoracic vertebra

1st free rib

2nd "true" rib

uncinate process rib 5

free rib

pectineal process

obturator foramen

ischiopubic fenestra

ischium

pubis

THORAX, PELVIS, CAUDA AND RIBS–RIGHT–LATERAL VIEW
PLATE 69

Plate 70   Thorax, Pelvis, Caudal, and Ribs   Dorsal View

Lumbar Vertebrae

The centra of the lumbar vertebrae are fused. The transverse processes of these vertebrae are fused to the ventral surface of ilium. The dorsal spines form a bridge between the dorsal crests of the ilii. The M. longissimus dorsi passes under this bridge. Parapophyses of the third and fourth lumbar vertebrae extend laterally from the centra of their respective vertebrae to unite with the ilium medioventrally in the cranial portion of the pectineal notch of the ilium.

Sacral Vertebrae

The sacral vertebrae form the caudal fourth of the pelvic roof by fusion of their dorsal spines and transverse processes. The lateral borders of the fused sacral vertebrae articulate with the medial border of the cranial iliac crest.

Synsacral Vertebrae

These six vertebrae form the caudal three-fourths of the pelvic roof. They are fused with the mediodorsal border of the ilium. Of this group, the sixth is fused with the first coccygeal vertebra by cartilagenous tissue.

Coccygeal Vertebrae

The coccygeal vertebrae (seven in number) are the tail vertebrae. The seventh is the pygostyle.

The dorsal spines of the first five caudal vertebrae are short and thick and bifurcate dorsally. The bifurcation increases the area for attachment of the M. levator caudae. The transverse processes are laterally directed and ventral spines are absent.

The seventh coccygeal vertebra (pygostyle) is directed dorsally and lacks transverse processes. The dorsal spine bifurcates. Caudal to the dorsal spine is the crest, a flat blade-like process, which ends in an apex. The cranial articular surface is just ventral to the neural canal. The haemal canal passes caudally and is bridged by a thin lamina of bone.

Ilium

The ilium extends caudally from the sixth thoracic rib to the caudal limit of the pelvic girdle.

The ilium is concave laterocranially and convex dorsocaudally. The crest of the ilium from cranial to caudal is S-shaped. The cranial portion of the crest forms the dorsal border of the ilium and the caudal portion forms its lateral border. The ilium forms the cranial, dorsal and part of the caudal borders of the acetabulum. The dorsal and the cranial border of the ilioischiadic foramen is formed by the ventrally-directed plate at the caudal aspect of the ilium.

In ventral view the ilium is concave. The M. obturator internus originates from the entire inner concavity of the ilium. Caudal to the ilioischiadic foramen is the obturator depression formed by the roof of the caudal ilium. The floor of the obturator depression is formed by a ventrolaterally-directed plate that fuses with the medial surface of the ischium.

Sternal Ribs

The cranial four sternal ribs articulate with the articular facets of the sternum. The fifth sternal rib is a false sternal rib since it articulates with the caudal process of the fourth sternal rib but does not reach the sternum proper. These ribs articulate dorsally with the third to the seventh thoracic rib.

The first four sternal ribs are short and three-sided with the apex of the triangle directed caudally. They become increasingly longer from the first through the fourth. The fifth sternal rib is flat but somewhat broadened at its thoracic rib articulation. The fifth sternal rib appears to have a caudal process at its dorsal end; however, this is a separate flattened bone that is firmly attached to the rib.

Ischium

The ischium extends caudally from the ventral border of the acetabulum and ends just beyond the caudal termination of the ilium. It lies ventral to the ilio-ischiadic foramen, lateral to the caudal crest of the ilium and dorsal to the obturator foramen and the pubis.

This bone is triangular, its apex forms most of the ventral border of the acetabulum. Its base lies between the caudal limits of the ilium and pubis.

The ischium forms the dorsal and caudal borders of the obturator foramen just ventral to the antitrochanter. The dorsal border of the ischio-pubic fenestra is formed by the ventral border of the ischium and is caudal to the obturator foramen.

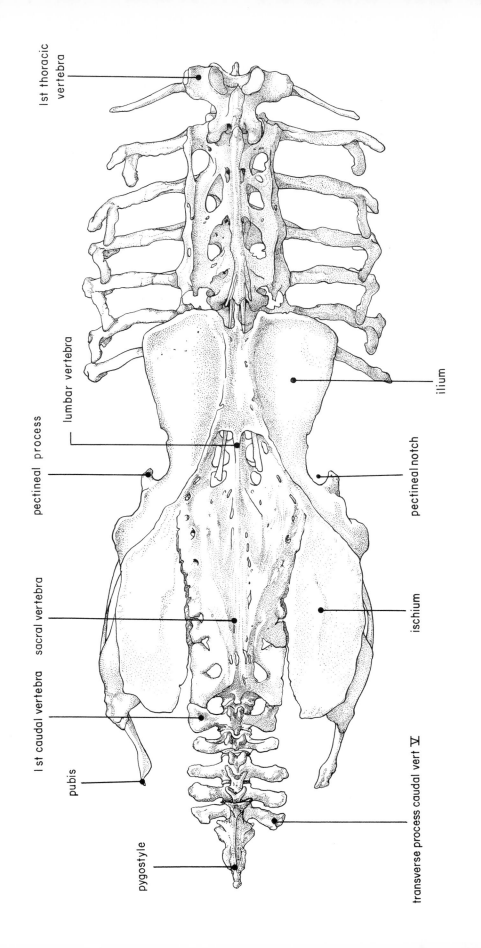

1st thoracic vertebra

lumbar vertebra

pectineal process

ilium

pectineal notch

sacral vertebra

1st caudal vertebra

ischium

pubis

transverse process caudal vert V

pygostyle

THORAX, PELVIS, CAUDA AND RIBS – DORSAL VIEW
PLATE 70

Plate 71   Thorax, Pelvis, Caudal, and Ribs   Ventral View

Pubis

The pubic bone is the most ventral of the pelvic girdle and extends about one-fifth its total length caudally beyond the ventral ischiatic angle. It is long and thin and at its cranial end forms a small portion of the cranio-ventral border of the acetabulum. The pectineal process extends from the pubis cranial to the acetabulum. The pubic bone caudal to the acetabulum forms the ventral border of the obturator foramen and the ischio-pubic fenestra.

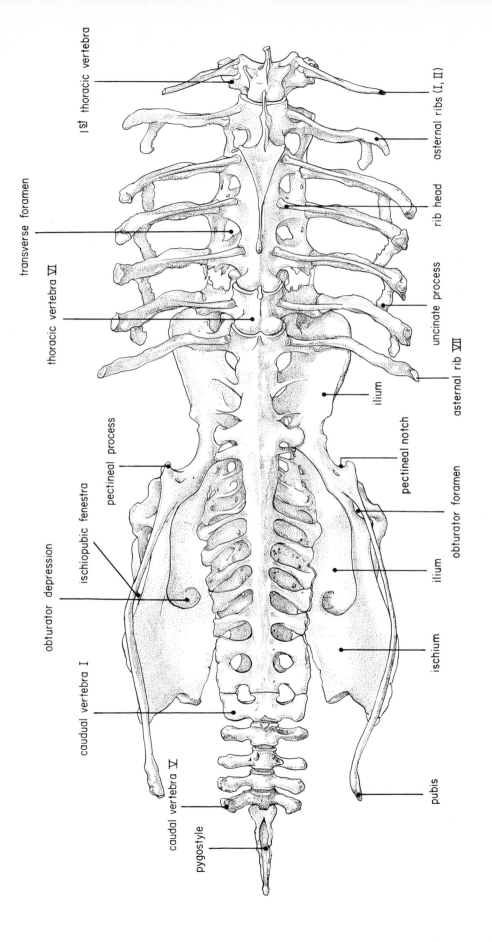

1st thoracic vertebra

asternal ribs (I, II)

transverse foramen

rib head

thoracic vertebra VI

uncinate process

asternal rib VII

ilium

pectineal process

pectineal notch

ischiopubic fenestra

obturator depression

ilium

obturator foramen

caudal vertebra I

ischium

caudal vertebra V

pubis

pygostyle

THORAX, PELVIS, CAUDA AND RIBS VENTRAL VIEW
PLATE 71

Plate 72   Furcula   Cranial and Caudal View

Furcula

The furcula is V-shaped with a short ventral process, the hypocleideum extending beyond the fusion (symphysis) of the right and left clavicles. The dorsal projections of the furcula articulate at their free ends in the furcular facets of the acromium of the coracoid. The ventral process is attached to the cranial carinal margin of the sternum by the hypocleideal ligament.

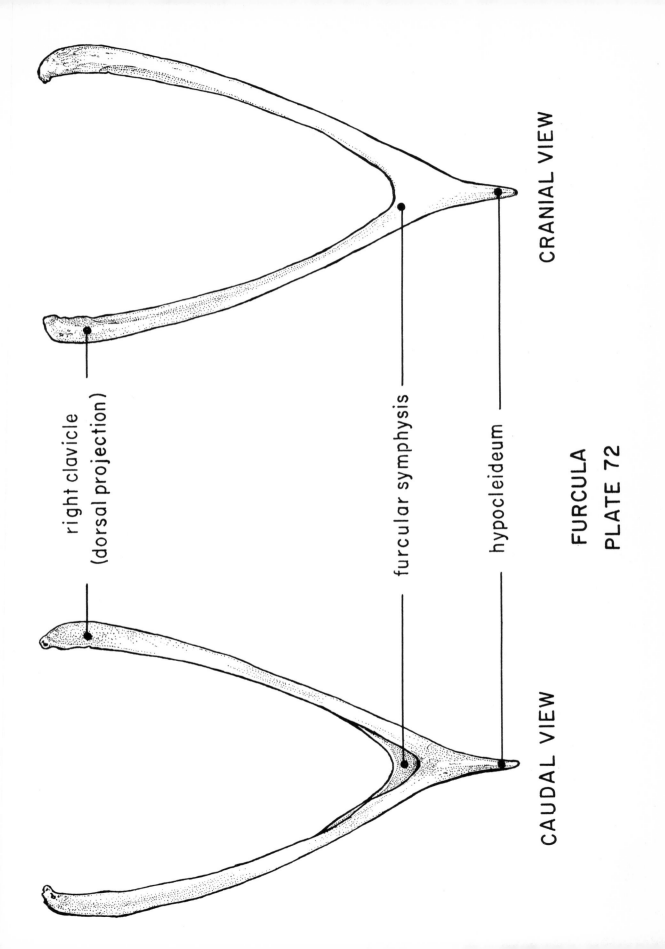

right clavicle
(dorsal projection)

furcular symphysis

hypocleideum

CRANIAL VIEW

CAUDAL VIEW

FURCULA
PLATE 72

Plate 73   Coracoid   Cranial and Caudal Views

Coracoid

The coracoid is lateral to the fourteenth cervical vertebra and extends
medioventrally from the shoulder apex to the cranial aspect of the sternum.

The ventral part of the coracoid flares out from the shaft and its ventral
surface articulates with the coracoidal articular sulci of the sternum.
The cranial face is smooth; the caudal face is rough and contains a pneumatic fossa and foramen. The shaft is tubular; the scapular facet is a
depression just dorsal to the caudal face of the shaft; medial to this is
the procoracoid tuberosity; and lateral and dorsal to this is the long
glenoid facet. Dorsal and medial to the glenoid facet is the acromium;
the furcula articulates on the cranial face of the acromium. The neck of
the coracoid lies between the procoracoid and the acromium.

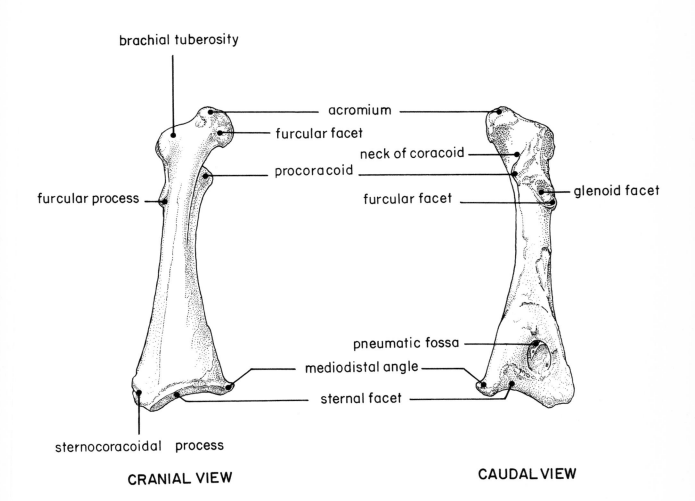

brachial tuberosity

acromium

furcular facet

neck of coracoid

procoracoid

furcular process

furcular facet

glenoid facet

pneumatic fossa

mediodistal angle

sternal facet

sternocoracoidal process

CRANIAL VIEW

CAUDAL VIEW

**CORACOID
PLATE 73**

Sternum

The sternum (breast bone) is carinate and the most ventral of the thoracic basket. The coracoid and furcula articulate with the sternum cranially and the sternal ribs articulate laterally.

At the dorsal aspect of the cranial carinal margin there is in the midline a ventral manubrial spine, and just dorsal to this spine is a dorsal manubrial spine.

The manubrial foramen is continuous between the right and left coracoidal articular sulci. The craniolateral process from which the M. sternocoracoideus originates has its base at the lateral extremity of the coracoidal articular sulcus and extends craniodorsally.

Four articular facets for sternal rib articulation are on the dorsal aspect of the craniolateral process.

The dorsolateral process caudal to the sternal rib facets is triangular shaped, whereas the caudolateral process is long and narrow.

At the level of the last sternal rib facet is a pneumatic fossa and foramen in the midline of the concave dorsal surface of the sternum.

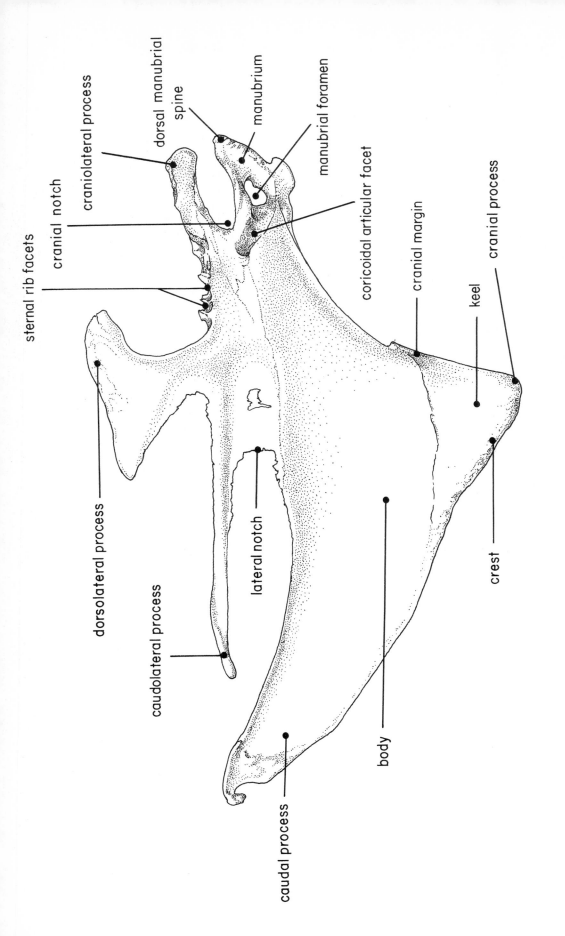

dorsal manubrial
spine

craniolateral process

cranial notch

sternal rib facets

dorsolateral process

caudolateral process

lateral notch

caudal process

body

crest

cranial process

keel

cranial margin

coricoidal articular facet

manubrial foramen

manubrium

STERNUM—RIGHT—LATERAL VIEW
PLATE 74

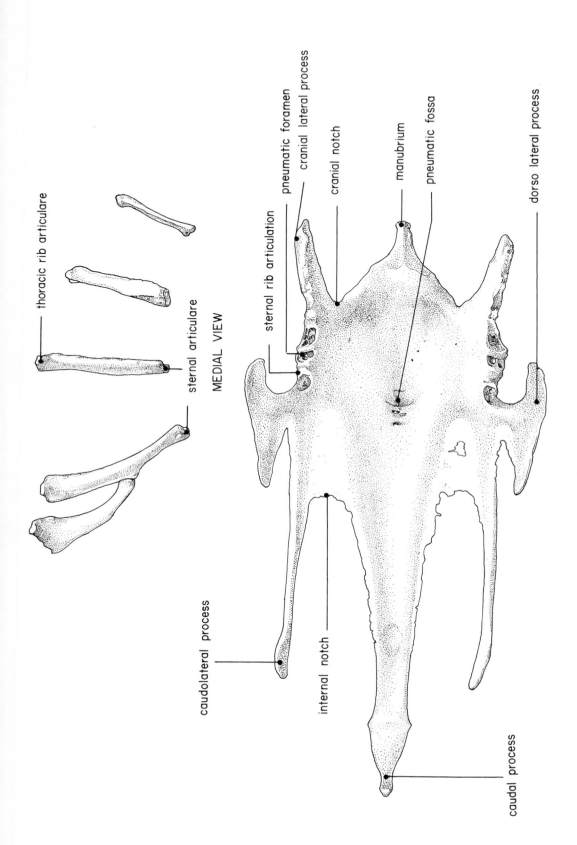

thoracic rib articulare

sternal articulare

MEDIAL VIEW

pneumatic foramen

cranial lateral process

cranial notch

manubrium

pneumatic fossa

dorso lateral process

sternal rib articulation

caudolateral process

internal notch

caudal process

DORSAL VIEW

STERNUM AND STERNAL RIBS
PLATE 75

Femur

The femur articulates proximally with the acetabulum, distally with the
tibiotarsus and the fibula.

The femur, seen from a medial view, has at its proximal end a prominent
ball-like process, the head. At the base of the ball of the femoral head
is the neck. Distally is a prominent medial (internal) condyle.

The lateral and medial epicondyles may be seen from the caudal view at the
lateral aspect distally on the femur. The most lateral is the fibular
condyle, medial to which is the lateral condyle. The fibular groove lies
between these condyles. The intercondylar fossa lies between the lateral
and medial condyles. The popliteal despression lies just proximal to the
intercondylar fossa.

The rotular groove lies between the lateral and medial condyles.

Patella (not shown)

The patella lies cranial to the articulation of the tibiotarsus and femur
but just proximal to the procnemial crest of the tibiotarsus. There are
two articulating surfaces on the patella: the lateral articular surface
that articulates with the lateral condyle of femur and the medial articular
surface articulates with intercondyloid surface of the medial condyle of
the femur.

On the dorsal surface of the patella a deep pectineal groove through which
passes the tendon of M. ambiens.

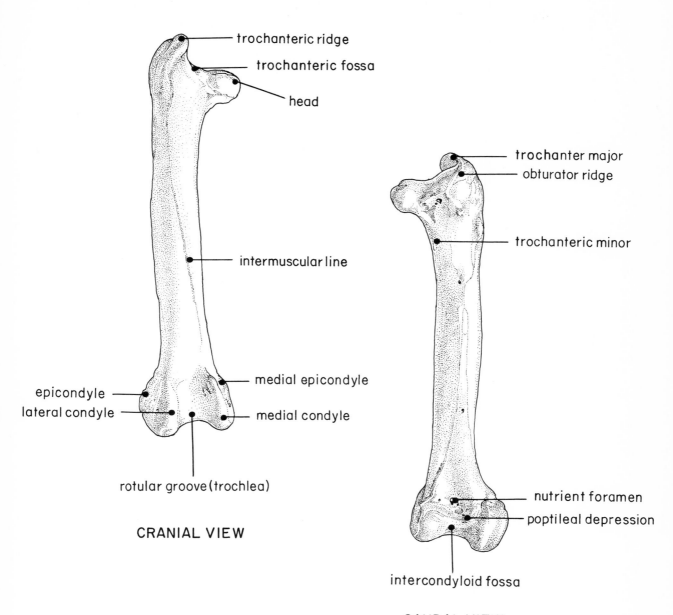

trochanteric ridge

trochanteric fossa

head

trochanter major

obturator ridge

trochanteric minor

intermuscular line

epicondyle

lateral condyle

medial epicondyle

medial condyle

rotular groove (trochlea)

CRANIAL VIEW

nutrient foramen

poptileal depression

intercondyloid fossa

CAUDAL VIEW

FEMUR—RIGHT
PLATE 76

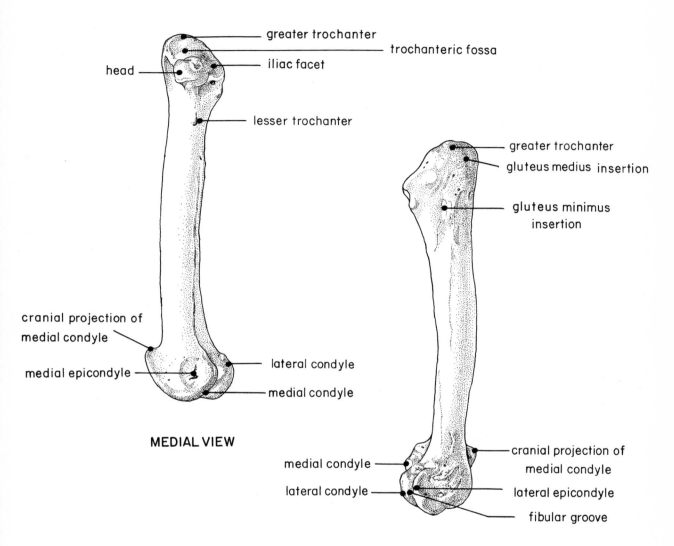

greater trochanter

trochanteric fossa

iliac facet

head

lesser trochanter

cranial projection of
medial condyle

medial epicondyle

lateral condyle

medial condyle

MEDIAL VIEW

greater trochanter

gluteus medius insertion

gluteus minimus
insertion

medial condyle

lateral condyle

cranial projection of
medial condyle

lateral epicondyle

fibular groove

LATERAL VIEW

**FEMUR – RIGHT
PLATE 77**

Tibiotarsus and Fibula

This is a composite bone and is fused in the mature bird. It includes the tibia, the fibula, and elements of the tarsus.

The tibiotarsus articulates proximally with the condyles of the femur and distally with the tarsometatarsus. The fibula is styloform and slightly fused laterally to the tibiotarsal portion of the composite. It extends distally two-thirds of the length of the tibiotarsus.

The proximal part of the tibiotarsus is angular. The cranial cnemial crest, a sharp prominent ridge, extends cranially. Lateral to this crest is the ventrally-directed angular lateral cnemial crest. The head of the tibiotarsus is demarked by a rotular crest.

The fibular head articulates with the tibiotarsus caudal to the lateral cnemial crest. The lateral articular surface articulates with the intercondylar fossa of the femur and the medial articular surface articulates with the medial condyle of the femur.

The fibula is fused to the fibular crest of the tibiotarsus distally and cranially to the head of the fibula.

A definite intermuscular line extends from the cranial cnemial crest distally on the shaft of the tibiotarsus. Distally on the cranial face of the shaft there is a tendinal groove covered by a bony supratendinal bridge, through which the tendon of the M. extensor digitorum pedis passes.

Lateral and medial condyles are at the distal extremity of this bone. A condylar fossa lies between the cranial surfaces of the condyles.

Distal to the fibular crest on the caudal surface of the tibiotarsus is the medullary artery foramen. Between the lateral and medial condyles is the caudal intercondylar sulcus and on the lateral and medial surfaces of the condyles are ligamental prominences.

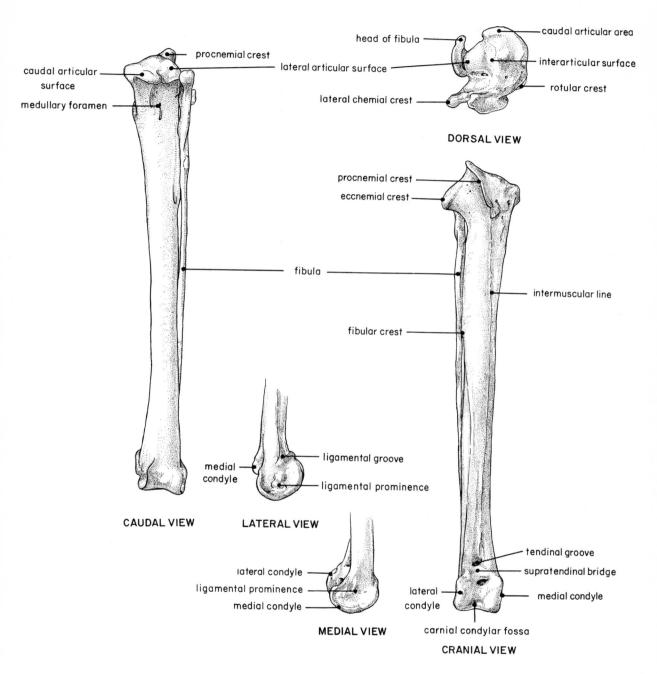

caudal articular surface
procnemial crest
caudal articular surface
medullary foramen
lateral articular surface

head of fibula
caudal articular area
interarticular surface
rotular crest
lateral chemial crest

DORSAL VIEW

procnemial crest
eccnemial crest

fibula

fibula

intermuscular line

fibular crest

ligamental groove
medial condyle
ligamental prominence

CAUDAL VIEW   **LATERAL VIEW**

tendinal groove
supratendinal bridge

lateral condyle
ligamental prominence
medial condyle

lateral condyle
medial condyle

carnial condylar fossa

MEDIAL VIEW

CRANIAL VIEW

TIBIOTARSUS AND FIBULA —RIGHT
PLATE 78

Plate 79   Tarsometatarsus - Right   Cranial, Caudal, and
Dorsal Views

Tarsometatarsus

The proximal end of the tarsometatarsus articulates with the condyles of
the tibiotarsus. At its distal end it has three trochlea for articulation
with the second, third and fourth digits.

The tarsometatarsus is a single bone; its proximal end is formed by the
fusion of the lower row of embryonic tarsals and the remaining distal
portion by fusion of the three embryonic metatarsals.

The hypotarsus is a caudal ridged process at the proximal extremity of the
tarsometatarsus. In the mature turkey an ossified tendon continues from the
achilles tendon and is inseparably fused at the medial ridge of the
hypotarsus. It continues two-thirds distally to a free point just beyond
the spur in males. This ossified tendon is concave-convex and the lateral
concave surface forms a groove for the M. flexor digiti pedis profundus.
A hypotarsal canal is formed by a bridge of bone lying between the medial
and the next lateral ridge of the hypotarsus. There are two nutrient
foramina, one each lying lateral and medial to the hypotarsus caudally.
Two other nutrient foramina lie in the interosseal fossa at the proximal
extremity of the tarsometatarsus cranially.

There are three trochlea distally, one for each of the three fused
metatarsals: II, III and IV. Metatarsal I is free. The most medial
trochlea is the smallest and articulates with digit II. The trochlear wing
forms a slight caudal process. The second and third trochlear are similar
in shape; however, the lateral is the smaller.

The second trochlea articulates with the digit III and the third trochlea
with the digit IV. The metatarsal of digit I articulates medially and
caudally one-half the distance between the spur and medial trochlea. This
metatarsal is concave plantarly and slightly convex dorsally. It is narrow
at its tarsometatarsus articulation and broad at its articulation with the
phalanx.

Just proximal to the lateral intertrochlear notch is the large distal
foramen. A foramen also is sometimes found in younger birds proximal to
the median intertrochlear notch.

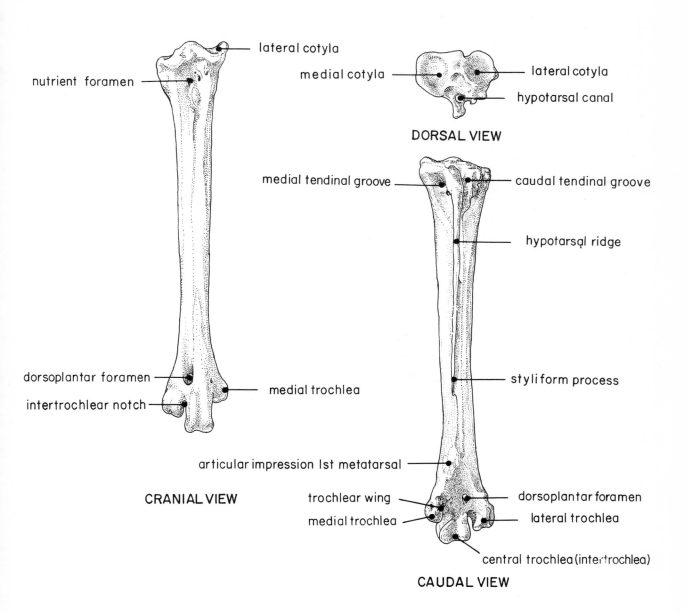

lateral cotyla

nutrient foramen

medial cotyla

lateral cotyla

hypotarsal canal

DORSAL VIEW

medial tendinal groove

caudal tendinal groove

hypotarsal ridge

dorsoplantar foramen

intertrochlear notch

medial trochlea

styliform process

articular impression 1st metatarsal

CRANIAL VIEW

trochlear wing

medial trochlea

dorsoplantar foramen

lateral trochlea

central trochlea (intertrochlea)

CAUDAL VIEW

TARSOMETATARSUS –RIGHT–(FEMALE)

PLATE 79

Plate 80   Tarsometatarsus - Right   Lateral and Medial Views

Hypotarsal Sesamoid

This sesamoid is found caudal to the trochlea of the tarsometatarsus. The articulating surface faces dorsally and cranially. Its medial surface is grooved for the passage of tendons. Its lateral surface is smooth and it is broader at its distal than its proximal end.

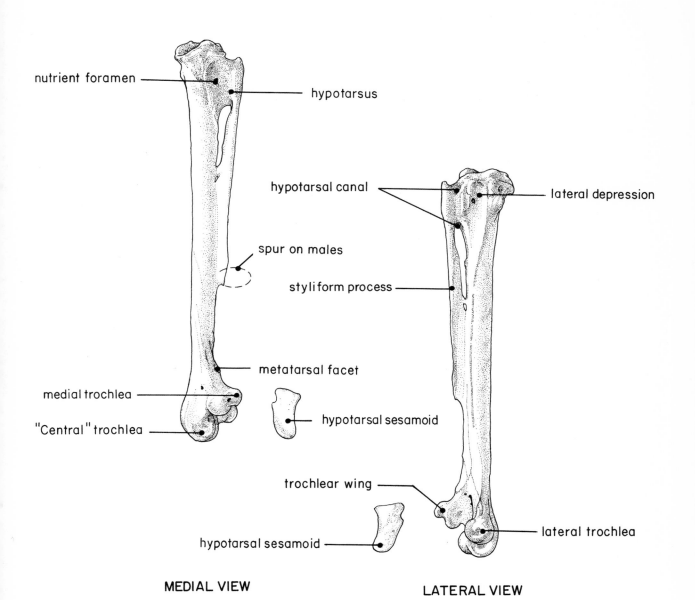

nutrient foramen

hypotarsus

hypotarsal canal

lateral depression

spur on males

styliform process

metatarsal facet

medial trochlea

hypotarsal sesamoid

"Central" trochlea

trochlear wing

hypotarsal sesamoid

lateral trochlea

MEDIAL VIEW

LATERAL VIEW

TARSOMETATARSUS – RIGHT – (FEMALE)
PLATE 80

Plate 81   Foot and Digits - Left   Dorsal View

Digits I, II, III, and IV

Digit I (the hallux) is directed obliquocaudally and articulates with the free metatarsal I. It is composed of two phalanges. The first phalanx of all digits is similar.

The articular fossa, proximal articulating surface, of the first phalanx is concave and enlarged. The distal articulating surface has a lateral and a medial condyle between which lies the intercondyloid sulcus. The second (ungual) phalanx of the hallux is claw-shaped and is typical of the terminal phalanges of the remaining digits.

All phalanges are convex dorsally and are flat to concave on their plantar surface.

Digit II has three phalanges and is directed cranially; its first phalanx articulates with the medial trochlea of the tarsometatarsus.

Digit III (middle toe) has four phalanges, is directed cranially and its first phalanx articulates with the third trochlea of the tarsometatarsus.

Digit IV has five phalanges and is directed craniolaterally. Its first phalanx articulates with the lateral trochlea of the tarsometatarsus.

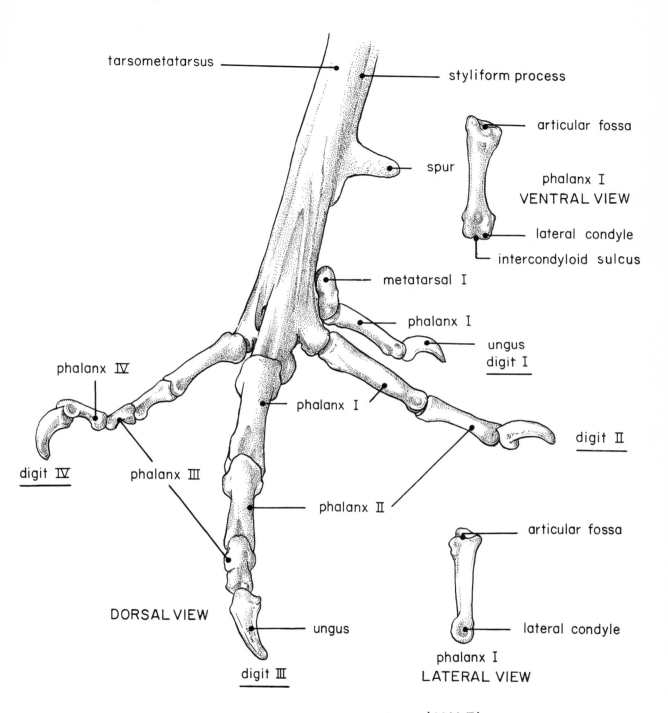

tarsometatarsus

styliform process

articular fossa

phalanx I
VENTRAL VIEW

spur

lateral condyle

intercondyloid sulcus

metatarsal I

phalanx I

ungus
digit I

phalanx IV

phalanx I

digit II

digit IV

phalanx III

phalanx II

articular fossa

ungus

lateral condyle

DORSAL VIEW

digit III

phalanx I
LATERAL VIEW

FOOT AND DIGITS —RIGHT –(MALE)
PLATE 81

Plate 82   Scapula - Right   Dorsal and Ventral Views

Scapula

The scapula lies over the thoracic ribs and its medial surface faces the lateral surface of these ribs near their thoracic vertebral articulation.

The head of the scapula articulates with the coracoid, humerus and the furcula. The caudal border of the blade of the scapula is near the cranial border of the ilium.

Viewed ventromedially, the scapula appears as a long narrow blade. The dorsal angle of the head is the furcular articulating process, whereas, its ventral angle is the coracoidal articulating process.

Along the dorsal edge of the blade, about three-fourths caudally, there is a convex angle (dorsal angle). Ventral to this is a concave angle (ventral angle). A pneumatic fossa is present in the scapula dorsolaterally just caudal to the furcular articulating process.

The glenoid facet ventral to the pneumatic fossa articulates with the humerus and the coracoid. The glenoid facet of the scapula and of the coracoid forms an articular socket for the head of the humerus.

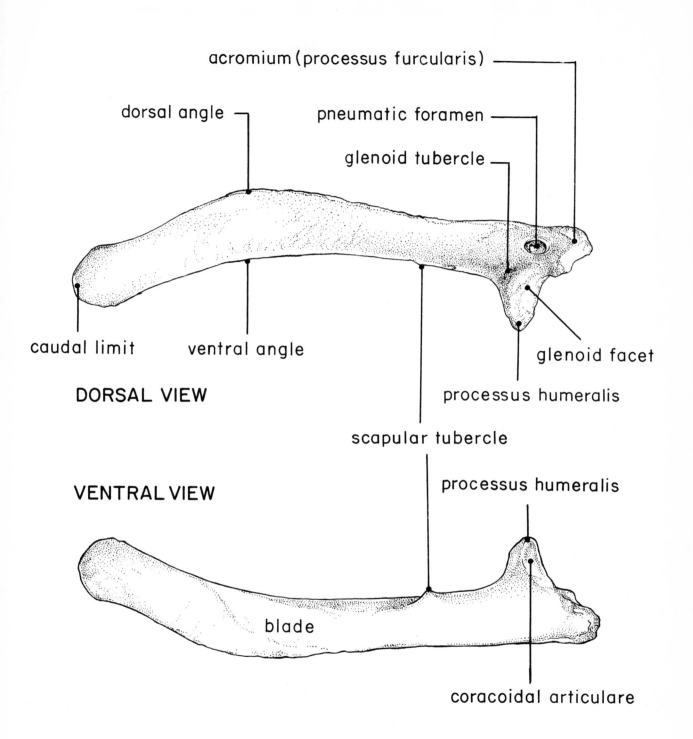

acromium (processus furcularis)

dorsal angle

pneumatic foramen

glenoid tubercle

caudal limit   ventral angle

glenoid facet

DORSAL VIEW

processus humeralis

scapular tubercle

VENTRAL VIEW

processus humeralis

blade

coracoidal articulare

SCAPULA – RIGHT
PLATE 82

Plate 83   Humerus - Right   Dorsal and Ventral Views

Humerus

The humerus lies in a horizontal plane; its head articulates with the glenoid fossa formed by the glenoid facets of the coracoid and scapula. The humerus articulates distally with the ulna and the radius.

Three sections of this bone may be seen from a lateral view: (1) the proximal expansion, (2) the shaft, and (3) the distal expansion.

The proximal expansion has a deltoid crest dorsally, a bicipital surface ventrally and a bicipital furrow between these two. A ligamental groove lies between the head and bicipital surface.

A well-marked brachial depression (origin for the M. brachialis) is on the laterodistal surface of the shaft.

The distal expansion has a trochlea formed dorsally by an external condyle and ventrally by an internal condyle, each have a roughened epicondyle externally. An ectepicondylar prominence is proximal to the external epicondyle.

From a medial view, the proximal expansion of the humerus has the following structures: proximally, the articular surface of the head, the bicipital ridge with a semicircular periphery, a pneumatic foramen dorsal to the bicipital ridge lies caudally to a prominent dorsoventral ridge which forms the caudal lip of the capitular groove.

The distal expansion is convex medially. The internal epicondylar ridge is seen distinctly in medial view. The olecranon fossa is a slight depression lying between the ridge and the epicondyle.

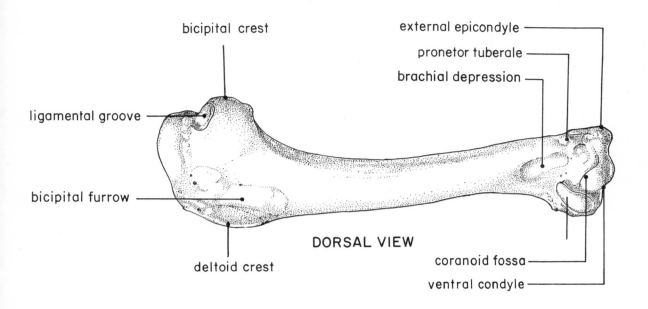

bicipital crest

external epicondyle

pronetor tuberale

brachial depression

ligamental groove

bicipital furrow

DORSAL VIEW

coranoid fossa

ventral condyle

deltoid crest

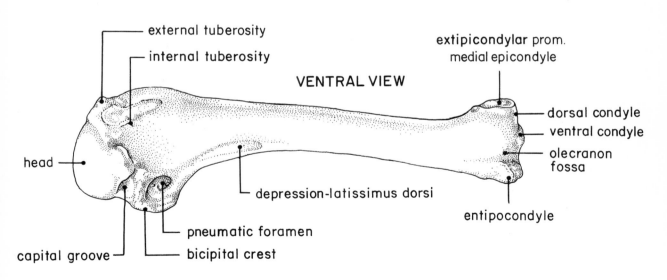

external tuberosity

internal tuberosity

VENTRAL VIEW

extipicondylar prom.
medial epicondyle

dorsal condyle

ventral condyle

head

olecranon
fossa

depression-latissimus dorsi

entipocondyle

pneumatic foramen

capital groove

bicipital crest

HUMERUS — RIGHT
PLATE 83

Plate 84   Radius and Ulna - Right   Dorsal and Ventral Views

Radius

The radius articulates proximally with the external condyle of the humerus, ventrally with the ulna, and distally with the radial carpal.

It is long and cylindrical with a round proximal articulating head, a shaft, and a flattened concave-convex distal articulating head. The radius is concave on its ulnar face and convex dorsally.

Ulna

The ulna articulates proximally with the internal condyle and to some extent with the external condyle of the humerus and with the head of the radius. Distally the ulna articulates with the radius, the ulnar carpal and the carpometacarpus.

The olecranon process is proximal. Just distal to this process or at its base is the internal cotyla (humeral articular surface). The external cotyla is a small area distal and lateral to the internal cotyla. A pronounced brachial depression lies distal to the internal cotyla.

At the distal extremity of the ulna the internal and external condyles form a trochlear surface. Just proximal to the internal condyle is a carpal tuberosity.

The external condylar ridge is prominent and extends from the concave to the convex surface where it forms a definite proximally directed process.

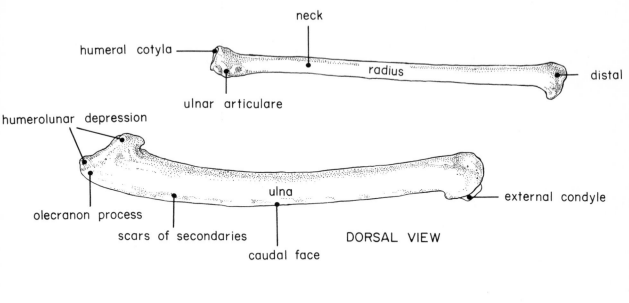

neck

humeral cotyla

radius

distal

ulnar articulare

humerolunar depression

olecranon process

scars of secondaries

ulna

external condyle

caudal face

DORSAL VIEW

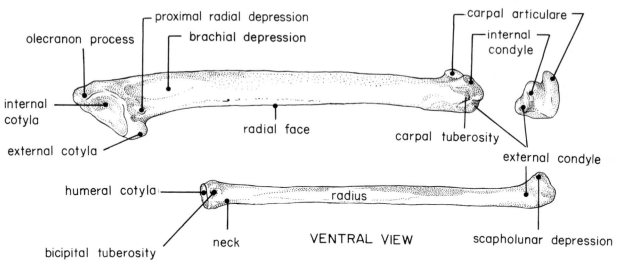

proximal radial depression

olecranon process

brachial depression

carpal articulare

internal condyle

internal cotyla

radial face

carpal tuberosity

external cotyla

external condyle

humeral cotyla

radius

bicipital tuberosity

neck

VENTRAL VIEW

scapholunar depression

RADIUS AND ULNA
PLATE 84

Plate 85   Carpometacarpus and Phalanges - Right   Dorsal and
                                                          Ventral Views

Carpometacarpus

The carpometacarpus articulates with the ulnar carpal, radial carpal and
ulna proximally and with digits II, III and IV distally.

The intermetacarpal process extends from metacarpal III over the intermetacarpal space and rests on metacarpal IV.

Metacarpal III is long and cylindrical and is thicker than the more
flattened metacarpal IV. These two bones are separated by an intermetacarpal space but meet proximally at the proximal metacarpal symphysis
and distally at the distal metacarpal symphysis. Metacarpal II is present
as only a process fused to the proximal end of metacarpal III. At the
distal extremity of metacarpal II is a facet for the articulation of
digit II. Articular facets for digits III and IV are present at the distal
extremities of metacarpals III and IV.

Digit II, III and IV

Digit II is composed of one phalanx that articulates at its proximal end
with metacarpal II. The phalanx is three-sided and tapers to a point at
its distal extremity.

Digit III is composed of two phalanges. The first is short and flat and
has a semicircular wing-like process that extends caudally. The second
phalanx is similar in shape to the phalanx of digit II.

Digit IV is composed of one short sturdy phalanx that articulates with
metacarpal IV.

Sesamoids

Carpometacarpal Sesamoid

This sesamoid is long and splint-shaped and is located cranially on
metacarpal III.

Ulnar Carpal

The ulnar carpal is distal to the ulna and along the convex surface just
proximal to the external condyle of the ulna. It articulates with the ulna
and carpometacarpus only.

The ulnar carpal is V-shaped, the internal surface articulating with the
carpometacarpus. The medial or anconal articulates with the ulna.

Radial Carpal

The radial carpal lies between the distal ends of the radius and ulna at the
proximal end of the carpometacarpus and has three articular surfaces. The
cotyloid, the most concave surface, articulates with the radius. On the
opposed side is the carpometacarpal articulating surface. The third articulating surface, the trochlear surface, is convex and articulates with the
trochlea of the ulna.

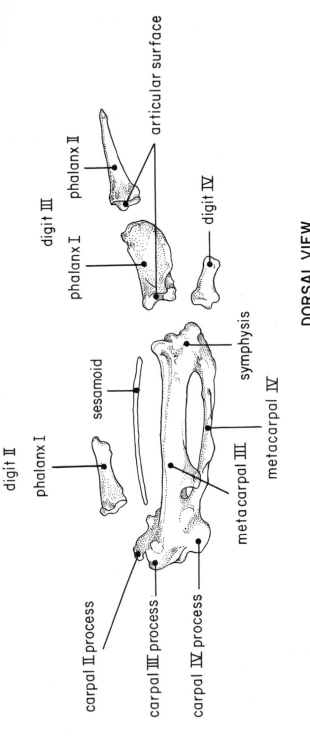

digit II

phalanx I

digit III

phalanx II

phalanx I

articular surface

digit IV

sesamoid

symphysis

metacarpal IV

metacarpal III

carpal II process

carpal III process

carpal IV process

DORSAL VIEW

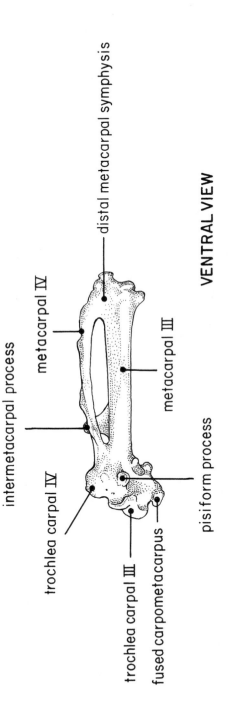

distal metacarpal symphysis

intermetacarpal process

metacarpal IV

metacarpal III

trochlea carpal IV

trochlea carpal III

fused carpometacarpus

pisiform process

VENTRAL VIEW

CARPOMETACARPUS AND PHALANGES – RIGHT

PLATE 85

BIBLIOGRAPHY

1. Anderson, R. J. (1900). "The crookedness in the sterna of certain breeds of domestic fowls," *Irish Nat.*, 9:150-52.
2. Asmundson, V. S. (1934). "The turkey as an experimental animal," *Am. Nat.*, 68:466-67.
3. Beddard, F. E. (1898). "The Structure and Classification of Birds," Longmans, Green, New York.
4. Berger, A. J. (1956). "Anatomical variation and avian anatomy," *Condor*, 58:433-41.
5. Berger, A. J. (1959). "Leg-muscle formulae and systematics," *Wilson Bull.*, 71:93-94.
6. Camper, P. (1773). "Memoire sur la structure des os dans les oiseaux et de leurs diversites dans les differentes especes," *Mem. math. phys. inst. fr.*, 7:328-35.
7. Chamberlain, F. W. (1943). *Atlas of the Avian Anatomy.* East Lansing, Michigan. Michigan State University Press.
8. Du Petit, F. (1738). "Description anatomique de l'oeil du coq d'inde," *Mem. acad. roy. sci.* for 1735, Paris, 123-53.
9. Elliot, D. G. (1872). *A Monograph of the Phasianidae or Family of the Pheasants*, Vol. I, New York.
10. Fisher, H. I. and D. C. Goodman (1955). "The Myology of the Whooping Crane, *Grus americana*," *Illinois Biol. Monographs* 24, (2).
11. Furbringer, M. (1886). "Uber Deutung und Nomenklatur der Muskulatur des Vogel-flugels," *Morphol. Jahrb.*, 11:121-25.
12. Furbringer, M. (1888). "Untersuchungen zur Morphologie und Systematik der Vogel, zugleich ein Beitrag zur Anatomie der Stutz- und Bewegungsorgane," 2 vols. Van Hokema, Amsterdam.
13. Gadow, H. (1880). "Zur vergleichenden Anatomie der Muskulatur des Beckens und der hinteren Gliedmassen der Ratiten," Fischer, Jena.
14. Gadow, H. and E. Selenka (1891). Aves In Bronn's "Klassen und Ordnungen des Thier-Reichs, in Wort und Bild," 2 vols., Anatomischer Theil, 1891, Systematischer Theil, 1893. Leipzig.
15. Garrod. A. H. (1881). "The Collected Scientific Papers of the Late Alfred Henry Garrod," (W. A. Forbes, ed.). R. H. Porter, London.
16. George, J. C. and A. J. Berger (1966). "Avian Myology," Academic Press, New York and London.
17. Howell, A. B. (1936a). "Morphogenesis of the shoulder architecture IV. Reptilia," *Quart. Rev. Biol.*, 11:183-208.
18. Howell, A. B. (1936b). "Phylogeny of the distal musculature of the pectoral appendage," *Jour. Morph.*, 60, (1) 287-315.

19. Howell, A. B. (1936c). "The phylogenetic arrangement of the muscular system," Anat. Rec., 66, (3) 295-316.
20. Howell, A. B. (1937). "Morphogenesis of the shoulder architecture: Aves," Auk, 54:363-75.
21. Howell, A. B. (1938a). "The muscles of the avian hip and thigh," Jour. Morph., 62:177-218.
22. Hudson, G. E., Lanzillotti, P. J., and Edwards, G. D. (1959). "Muscles of the pelvic limb in galliform birds," Am. Midland Naturalist, 61:1-67.
23. Jackson, J. B. S. (1895). "Malformed sternum of a turkey," Proc. Boston Soc. Nat. Hist. for 1874-75, 17:454.
24. Kaupp, B. F. (1918). Anatomy of the Domestic Fowl. Philadelphia, Saunders.
25. Latimer, H. B. (1926). "A quantitative study of the anatomy of the turkey hen," Anat. Rec., 34:15-23.
26. Latimer, H. B. (1927). "Correlations of the weights and lengths of the body, systems and organs of the turkey hen," Anat. Rec., 35:365-77.
27. Montagna, W. (1945). "A reinvestigation of the development of the wing of the fowl," Jour. Morphol., 76:87-113.
28. Nelson, E. W. (1900). "Description of a new subspecies of Meleagris gallopavo and proposed changes in the nomenclature of certain North American birds," Auk, 17:120-23.
29. Newton, A. and Gadow, H. (1893-1896). "A Dictionary of Birds," Adam & Charles Black, London.
30. Owen, R. (1837). "Dissection of the head of the turkey buzzard and that of the common turkey," Proc. Zool. Soc. London, 5:34-35.
31. Parker, W. K. (1866). "On the osteology of gallinaceous birds and tinamous," Trans. Zool. Soc. London, 5:149-241.
32. Retterer, E. and A. Lelievre (1911). "Phenomenes cytologiques des tendons en voie d'ossification," Comp. rend. soc. biol., Paris, 71:596-99.
33. Romer, A. S. (1927). "The development of the thigh musculature of the chick," Jour. Morphol. Physiol., 43:347-385.
34. Shorger, A. W. (1963). "The domestic turkey in Mexico and Central America in the Sixteenth Century," Wis. Acad. Sci., 52:133-52.
35. Shorger, A. W. (1966). "The Wild Turkey: Its History and Domestication," University of Oklahoma Press, Norman, Oklahoma.
36. Shufeldt, R. W. (1887a). "A critical comparison of a series of skulls of the wild and domesticated turkeys," Jour. Comp. Med. and Surg. New York, 8:207-22.
37. Shufeldt, R. W. (1887b). "The turkey skull," Am. Nat., 21:777.

38. Shufeldt, R. W. (1890). "The Myology of the Raven (Dorvus corax sinuatus)."

39. Shufeldt, R. W. (1909). "Osteology of Birds," N. Y. State Mus. Bull., 130.

40. Shufeldt, R. W. (1914). "On the skeleton of the ocellated turkey (Agriocharis ocellata), with notes on the osteology of other meleagridae," Aquila, 21:1-52.

41. Stressman, E. (1959). "The status of avian systematics and its unsolved problems," Auk, 75:269-80.

42. Tiedemann, D. F. (1814). Anatomie und Naturgeschichte der Vogel. Vol. II. Heidelberg.

43. Wagner, R. (1837). "Beitrage zur Anatomie der Vogel," Abh. Akad. d. Wiss. Munich, 2:271-308.

44. Wetmore, A. (1956). "A check-list of the fossil and prehistoric birds of North America and the West Indies," Smith. Mis. Colls., 131(5).

INDEX

A. <u>Myology</u>

INDEX

B. <u>Osteology</u>

☆ U.S. GOVERNMENT PRINTING OFFICE : 1968 O—319-833